D1188469

RICHARD RAYNAL,

SOLITARY

RICHARD RAYNAL,
SOLITARY

by *ROBERT HUGH BENSON*

WITH AN INTRODUCTION BY EVELYN WAUGH

ILLUSTRATED BY VALENTI ANGELO

CHICAGO · HENRY REGNERY COMPANY · 1956

PATRI · REVERENDISSIMO

✹. ✹✹✹✹. ✹✹✹✹✹✹. ✹.✹.✹.

ET

CVIDAM · NESCIENTI

HVNC · LIBRVM

D.

Preface

The History of Richard Raynal, Solitary was written at Cambridge in 1905, when Robert Hugh Benson was in his thirty-fifth year, his first in the Catholic priesthood. He had been received into the Church in September 1903 and had gone straight to Rome where by a special privilege the studies normally required of a converted Anglican clergyman were curtailed to satisfy his impatient wish for ordination. It was the intention of his superiors that he should continue his theological reading for a year while he found his way in the new world he had entered and decided where in it lay his own particular place. Accordingly he went to live without pastoral duties in the house of a congenial prelate, Mgr. Barnes. The place was full of associations for him. He had been an undergraduate at Trinity like his father and brothers before him and one brother, Arthur, was a don at Magdalene. He read some Theology but instead of enjoying the tranquility designed for him, he mixed freely in the University, charming everyone, and

vii

composed three complete books, surrendering himself to the nervous energy which always possessed and finally consumed him. Indecision about his vocation persisted throughout his short life and is implicit in most of his fiction.

He was the youngest and third surviving son of Edward White Benson, an eminent Victorian, who from modest beginnings serenely rose by sheer merit to the highest position in the kingdom, the Archbishopric of Canterbury. The personality of the holder determines how far power coincides with precedence in that office. Archbishop Benson was a man of great authority, simple piety and enormous industry. He was a broad churchman for whom Rome had no attraction. As a practical statesman he realized the futility of the hazy notions of re-union that were then prevalent among some of his colleagues, and he ostentatiously eschewed all discussion of the topic. Instead he promoted friendly association with Protestant non-conformists and with the heretical eastern churches and mitigated his predecessors' severity towards ritualists, whom he confirmed in such hitherto illegal practices as the use of altar lights and the mixed chalice. He died when Hugh was 25, newly ordained in the Church of England, and already identified with the extreme high church party.

Both Hugh's brothers, who outlived him by many years, became prominent writers, E. F. Benson as a prolific and popular social satirist, Arthur as an essayist, biographer and finally as head of his college. Both had great facility; both were more exact scholars than Hugh, whose election to College at Eton at the age of twelve was his sole academic success. Neither showed any of his spiritual intensity or theological predilections. Neither married, and it may be conjectured that celibacy was never a problem to Hugh. Indeed there is a sense in which it may be said that Hugh had no problems. His faith was childlike and complete, open to the criticisms of excessive credulity. When asked by the Dominican preparing him to propound his doubts, he was unable to name one. Neither the general biological or archaeological worries of the age, nor the specific Anglican difficulties affected him at all.

He found his way into the Church by an easy route and once there, never once doubted that it was the right and only place for him or for anyone else. Superficially he was very much an aesthete, but the Catholic Church made little aesthetic appeal to him. He loved the music of King's College chapel, the architecture of the English parish houses, the prose of Cranmer. He had no taste for Italian baroque. What he sought and found in the Church was authority and catholicity. A national church, however wide the empire (and in his life time the empire seemed boundless and indestructible), could never speak with universal authority and, because it was provincial, it was necessarily narrow, finding room for scandalous doctrinal aberrations but forever incapable of enclosing the vast variety of humanity. Transplanted the Church of England became merely the church of the golf club and the garrison. Hugh as an Anglican clergyman made starts in various directions, in the slums of London, in a rural parish, in a community. In all he was zealous and popular. When after eight years he left the Church of England there was no bitterness on his side and very few reproaches from his former associates. Such intellectual fidgets as he suffered concerned rather light matters such as the nature of ghosts and the immortality of domestic animals.

This is not to say that he was perfectly at ease in the Church either then or later. He rejoiced in the picturesque diversity of a body which included saints and brigands and Borgias of both these categories, but he was a highly irritable man and a great deal got on his nerves. He did not like the aristocratic salons of Rome or the plebeian presbyteries of England, he deplored the smug conventions of the English ruling class, but recoiled from any whiff of real Bohemia. He hated no one but a great many people bored him and made him shy. His own personality was his prime problem.

In seeking his own salvation and in directing others, he took as his guide the saying of the Abbé Huvelin: 'il faut respecter le type que Dieu cherche á produire en nous.' What was the type which God was seeking to produce in Hugh Benson? His gifts were many and attractive. He had exquisite, light-hearted social manners. He was musical and keenly appreciative of visual beauty. His drawings are lively and untutored—rather bad, in fact, but to draw badly is a better way of keeping the eye in training than not to draw at all. He was a magnetic preacher, an excellent story-teller, a ready writer; he had enthusiasm and unremitting energy, a rich imagination, an exuberant curiosity about people and things. But he knew that there was only one relationship of absolute value, that of the soul to God. How was he to approach God, how best serve him? He saw himself from time to time as a Dominican, an Oratorian, a Benedictine, as a secular priest in the United States, as the specialized director of difficult souls, as an anchorite, as the founder of a pious, artistic, lay community. In each of his novels one can see a sketch of what he thought might possibly be the type which God was seeking to produce in him.

For this reason, that he always secreted a higher aspiration, he often seemed frivolous particularly about his own achievements.

'Why don't you take more trouble on your novels?' he was asked. 'If a thing's worth doing at all, it's worth doing well."

'I totally disagree,' he answered. 'There are lots of things which are worth doing, but aren't in the least worth doing *well.*'

Such light remarks, repeated out of their context, give a false impression. He was never cynical about his writing. While engaged on it, he worked with zest. But he did not hold the Flaubertian doctrine of the dedication of the artist. He would not have denied that this might be another's vocation. It was not his. A life spent in the laborious perfection of form was to him a life of vanity. A literary reputation was merely human respect. He worked without thought of posterity, as though Doomsday were imminent, using all his talents lavishly to draw as many souls as possible among his immediate neighbors to their true end in God.

Inevitably his reputation suffered and with it his power for good. Posterity is a discriminating customer and demands goods of the highest quality. The public for whom he wrote has now gone to its judgment and during the last twenty-five years his novels have been generally regarded as wholesome reading for school children, and nothing more. Lately however there has been a quickening of interest. Adults have begun to recapture some of the zest which went into these stories and to realize that they compare well with the general run of contemporary bestsellers. It is a welcome sign that the 'Thomas More Books to Live' series, which has shown such flair in reissuing partly forgotten Catholic writings, should have chosen one of Hugh Benson's for their enterprising list.

Richard Raynal, solitary is a good choice. Though it is far from typical of the author's work it was always his favorite. His other books are direct propaganda. He set himself three tasks: first to rewrite in popular form the history of the English reformation. In this series he is as robustly tendentious as Charles Kingsley had shown himself on the Protestant side. He opened the way for the more exact scholarship and deeper historical imagination of Mr. Alfred Duggan and Miss H. F. M. Prescott. Secondly he wrote vivid contemporary romances in which unusual characters are showing their peculiar vocations by the light of supernatural revelation working through unusual agents. Thirdly he essayed the novel of the future, presenting in two vivid pictures the possible course of world history according to whether posterity accepted or rejected the divine promises. All these books had their success at the time and doubtless will do so again. But *Richard Raynal* is something different. It can best be described as a piece of ecclesiastical decorative art, comparable to a tapestry by Burne-Jones or a painting by Holman-Hunt.

At the time of writing Hugh Benson was briefly but deeply under the influence of Frederick Rolfe. Fr. Martindale, in his full and admirable biography, said little about this striking character. Since the publication of A. J. Symons's *Quest for Corvo* the need for reticence is past. Frederick Rolfe, though less than Byronic, was certainly 'mad, bad and dangerous to know.' It took Benson three years to discover this. When he did, he dropped him, promptly and without remorse, and was pursued by vilification as Rolfe became yearly more desperate and abandoned to vice. But there was concealed in Rolfe's odious personality the germs of genius and so far as he influenced *Richard Raynal* he was purely beneficial.

The story is elaborately disguised as the translation of a manuscript discovered in Rome. This was a literary trick rather fashionable at the time. It was not meant to deceive. No one with any acquaintance with fifteenth century literature could mistake the author's intention; as well charge William Morris with forging medieval il-

luminated manuscripts. Benson was much dismayed to
find that some readers thought themselves hoaxed. The
innocent mystification may be regarded merely as a richly
tooled binding. He had grown up in buildings of the late
Middle Ages at Lincoln, Lambeth, Eton and Cambridge.
His young imagination had created a brilliant vision of
those times. In *Richard Raynal* he is describing this fanciful epoch, not historical reality. The simple story is told
more obscurely and more elaborately than in any of his
historical books. The beautiful hermit idyllically happy
in his solitude is called to deliver a single message to the
great world. He has to prepare the saintly King—Henry
VI—for his passion and death. Brutal and insidious attempts are made to frustrate his mission. Finally in his
own person he enacts the suffering of his king and dies in
the king's bed. There is more than a hint of the ancient
magic of European kingship—the royal priest-victim of
the *Golden Bough*—and the curious can no doubt find nu-
merous allusions to occult practices with which Rolfe
claimed familiarity. But it can best be read, I think, as an
allegory of one of the types which Benson thought God
might be seeking to produce in him. He was never able to
reconcile the conflicting call of solitude and contemplation with that of direct intervention—often rather drastic
intervention—in the lives of others. One part of him was

eminently sociable. To see him among his friends bub-
bling over with fun and ghost stories, it was hard to know
that he was always shielding one huge part of his life from
them. He believed he must be accessible to anyone who
needed his help and he believed, rightly, that there were
certain kinds of help to certain kinds of persons which he
was eminently fitted to offer. But those who confided in
him and profited by his advice were often disconcerted to
find that no abiding personal relationship had been established. He was inclined to leave them as a surgeon
leaves his patient after a successful operation. More than
this, those he singled out for affection repeatedly vexed
and disappointed him. He had the story-teller's fault of
attributing to them alien characteristics.

He had no call to poverty. Though ascetic in his way of
life he lacked the impulse to surrender himself to provi-
dence, which is the essential of the ideal of poverty. He
needed very few worldly goods or comforts but he had the
Victorian insistence on a small but secure and regular in-
come. Thus he saw his hermitage, when it came to translation into real life, as his picturesque house at Hare
Street, surrounded by pious and cultured gentlemen who
would live together frugally, industriously and prayer-
fully. This ideal was never realized. In the last week of
his life he was talking of leaving Hare Street and settling

with the Benedictines at Caldey. He never found his vocation. Or rather the fulfilment of his vocation proved to be
a brief life of throwing himself wholeheartedly into the
tasks which turned up while always rather wistfully
glancing over his shoulder towards a more perfect, un-
realized manner of service.

Richard Raynal remained the expression of his earliest
dream—the recluse with the single, vital message. It still
has the charm of that fresh enthusiasm.

EVELYN WAUGH

CONTENTS

Contents—CONTINUED

RICHARD RAYNAL,
SOLITARY

Introduction

In the winter of 1903-4 I had occasion
to pass several months in Rome.

Among other Religious Houses, lately bought back
from the Government by their proper owners, was one
(whose Order, for selfish reasons, I prefer not to spec-
ify), situated in the maze of narrow streets between the
Piazza Navona and the Piazza Colonna; this, however,
may be said of the Order, that it is one which, although
little known in Italy, had several houses in England up
to the reign of Henry VIII. Like so many other Orders at
that time, its members moved first to France and then to
Italy, where it has survived in penurious dignity ever
since.

The Religious were able to take with them at the time
of exodus, three and a half centuries ago, a part of the
small library that existed at the English mother-house,
and some few of these MSS. have survived to the present
day; many others, however, have certainly perished; for
in the list of books that I was looking over there one day

1

in March, 1904, I observed several titles, of which, the priest-librarian told me, the corresponding volumes have disappeared. To some half-dozen of these titles, however, there was appended a star, and on enquiring the meaning of this symbol, I was informed that it denoted that a translation had been made into French and preserved in the library.

One of these titles especially attracted my attention. It ran as follows: VITA ET OBITUS DNI RICARDI RAYNAL HEREMITAE.

Upon my asking to see this and its companions, I was conducted to a dusty shelf in the little upstairs bookroom, and was informed that I might do as I pleased there for two hours, until the Ave Maria *rang, and the doors would be locked.*

When the librarian had gone with many nods and smiles, I took down these half-dozen books and carried them to the table by the window, and until Ave Maria *rang I turned their pages.*

The volume whose title had especially attracted my attention was a quarto MS., written, I should suppose from the caligraphy, about the end of the sixteenth century; a later hand had appended a summary to each chapter with an appropriate quotation from a psalm. But the book was in a shocking condition, without binding, and contained no more than a fragment. The last page was numbered "341," and the first page "129." One hundred and twenty-eight pages, therefore, were certainly lost at the beginning, and I know not how many at the end; but what was left was sufficiently engrossing to hold me standing by the window, until the wrinkled face of the priest looked in again to inform me that unless I wished to sleep in the library, I must be gone at once.

On the following morning by nine o'clock I was there again; and, after an interview with the Superior, went up again with the keys in my own possession, a quantity of foolscap and a fountain-pen in my hand, and sandwiches in my pocket, to the dusty little room beneath the roof.

I repeated this series of actions, with the exception of the interview, every day for a fortnight, and when I returned to England in April I took with me a complete re-translation into English of the "Vita et obitus Dni Ricardi Raynal Heremitae," and it is this re-translation that is now given to the public, with the correction of many words and the addition of notes, carried out during the last eighteen months.

It is necessary to give some account of the book itself,

3

but I will not trouble my readers with an exhaustive survey of the reasons that have led me to my opinions on the subject: it is enough to say that most of them are to be found in the text.

It is the story of the life of one of that large body of English hermits who flourished from about the beginning of the fourteenth century to the middle of the sixteenth; and was written, apparently for the sake of the villagers, by his parish-priest, Sir John Chaldfield, *who seems to have been an amiable, devout, and wordy man, who long outlived his spiritual son. Of all the early part of* Master Richard Raynal's *life we are entirely ignorant, except of the facts that his parents died in his youth, and that he himself was educated at* Cambridge. *No doubt his early history was recorded in the one hundred and twenty-nine pages that are missing at the beginning. It is annoying also that the last pages are gone, for thereby we have lost what would probably have been a very full and exhaustive list of the funeral furniture of the sixteenth century, as well as an account of the procession into the country and the ceremonies observed at the burial. We might have heard, too, with some exactness (for* Sir John *resembles a journalist in his love of detail) about the way in which his friend's fame began to*

4

*spread, and the pilgrims to journey to his shrine. It
would have been of interest to trace the first stages in
the unauthorised cult of one as yet uncanonised. What
is left of the book is the record of only the last week in*
Master Richard's *life and of his death under peculiar
circumstances at* Westminster *in the bed-chamber of the
King.*

*It is impossible to know for certain who was this king,
but I am inclined to believe that it was* Henry VI., *the
founder of Eton College and King's College, Cambridge,
whose life ended in such tragedy towards the close of the
fifteenth century. His Queen is not mentioned from beginning to end, and for this and other reasons I am inclined to particularise still more, and conjecture that the
period of which the book treats must be prior to the
year 1445 AD., when the King married at the age of
twenty-three.*

*Supposing that these conjectures are right, the cardi-
nal spoken of in the book would be* Cardinal Beaufort,
Bishop of Winchester, *and cousin of the King.*

*All this, however, must be doubtful, since the trans-
lator of the original English or Latin appears to have
omitted with scrupulous care the names of all person-
ages occurring in the narrative, with one or two unim-*

portant exceptions. We do not even know in what part of the country Sir John Chaldfield *held his living, but it appears to have been within thirty or forty miles of London. We must excuse the foreign scribe, however; probably the English names were unintelligible and barbarous to his perceptions; and appeared unimportant, too, compared to the interest of the mystical and spiritual experiences recorded in the book.*

Of these experiences it is difficult to write judiciously in this practical age.

Master Richard Raynal *appears to have been a very curious young man, of great personal beauty, extreme simplicity, and a certain magnetic attractiveness. He believed himself, further, to be in direct and constant communication with supernatural things, and would be set down now as a religious fanatic, deeply tinged with superstition. His parson, too, in these days, would be thought little better, but at the time in which they lived both would probably be regarded with considerable veneration. We hear, in fact, that a chapel was finally erected over* Master Raynal's *body, and that pilgrimages were made there; and, probably, if the rest of the work had been preserved to us, we should have found a record of miracles wrought at his shrine. All traces, however,*

6

of that shrine have now disappeared—mostly likely un-
der the stern action of Henry VIII.—and Richard's *name*
is unknown to hagiology, in spite of his parson's confi-
dence as regarded his future beatification.

It is, however, interesting to notice that in Master
Raynal's *religion, as in Richard Rolle's, hermit of Ham-*
pole, there appears to have been some of that inchoate
Quietism which was apt to tinge the faith of a few of the
English solitaries. He was accustomed to attend mass de-
voutly and to receive the sacraments, and on his death-
bed was speeded into the next world, at his own desire,
by all the observances prescribed by the Catholic Church.
His attitude, too, towards the priesthood, is somewhat
uncharacteristic of his fellows, who were apt to boast
with apparent complacency that they were neither "monk,
friar, nor clerk." In other matters he is a good type of
that strange race of solitaries who swarmed in England
at that time, who were under no vows, but served God
as it pleased them, not hesitating to go among their fel-
lows from time to time if they thought themselves called
to it, who were looked upon with veneration or contempt,
according to the opinion formed of them by their observ-
ers, but who, at any rate, lived a simple and wholesome
life, and were to some extent witnesses to the existence

7

of a supernatural Power at whose bidding (so they be-lieved) they were summoned to celibacy, seclusion, la-bour, and prayer.

It is curious also to trace through Sir John's fanciful eyes the parallels between the sufferings of Master Rich-ard and those of Christ. Of course, no irreverence is in-tended. I should imagine that, if Sir John were put on his defence, he would say that the life of every true Christian must approximate to the life of Christ so far as his spirit is identified with the Divine Spirit, and that this is occasionally fulfilled even in minute details.

It is unnecessary to add much more in this introduc-tion—(for the story will tell its own tale)—beyond say-ing that the re-translation of the French fragment into English has been to me a source of considerable pleas-ure. I have done my best to render it into the English of its proper period, including even its alliterations, while avoiding needless archaisms and above all arbitrary spelling. But no doubt I am guilty of many solecisms. I have attempted also to elucidate the text by a number of footnotes, in which I have explained whatever seemed to call for it, and have appended translations to the nu-merous Latin quotations in which Sir John indulges after the manner of his time. I must apologise for these footnotes—(such are always tiresome)—but I could think of no other way by which the text could be made clear. They can always be omitted without much loss by the reader who has no taste for them.

Sir John's style is a little difficult sometimes, especially when he treats in detail of his friend's mystical experience, but he has a certain power of word-painting (unusual at his date) in matters both of nature and of grace, and it is only when he has been unduly trite or obscure that I have ventured, with a good deal of regret, to omit his observations. All such omissions, however, as well as peculiar difficulties of statement or allusion, have been dealt with in foot-notes.

With regard to the function of the book, at any rate since its first translation into French, it is probably safe to conjecture that it may have been used at one time for reading aloud in the refectory. I am led to make this guess from observing its division into chapters, and the quasi-texts appended to each. These texts are of all sorts, though all are taken from the Book of Psalms; but their application to the matter that follows is sometimes fanciful, frequently mystical, and occasionally trite.

If the book receives any sympathy from English readers—(an eventuality about which I have my doubts)— I shall hope, at some future date, to edit others of the MSS. still reposing in the little room under the roof be-

tween *the* Piazza Navona *and the* Piazza Colonna *in Rome, to which I have been generously promised free access.*

I must express my gratitude to the Superior of the Order of — — (to whose genius, coupled with that of another, I dedicate this book), for giving me permission to edit his MS.; to Dom Robert Maple, O.S.B., for much useful information and help in regard to the English mystics; and to Mme. Germain who has verified references, interpreted difficulties, and assisted me by her encouragement.

ROBERT BENSON.

Cambridge,

Feast of SS. Peter and Paul, 1905.

10

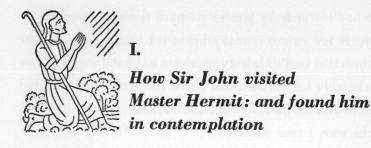

I.

How Sir John visited Master Hermit: and found him in contemplation

Protexit me in abscondito tabernaculi sui.

He hath protected me in the secret place of His tabernacle.
—*Ps. xxvi.* 5.

[*The MS. begins abruptly at the top of the page.*]

... IT was at vespers on the fourth day afterwards, being Corpus Christi, that saint Giles, as I suppose, moved me to visit Master Richard. So I put on my cap again, and took my furred gown, for I thought it would be cold before I came home; and set out through the wood. I was greatly encouraged by the beauty of the light as I went down; the sun shone through the hazels on my right, and the roof of leaves was a fair green over my head; and to right and left lay a carpet of flowers as blue as the Flanders' glass above the altar.

11

I had learnt from Master Richard though he was thirty years my younger, many beautiful lessons, and one of them that God's Majesty speaks to us by the works of His almighty hands. So when I saw the green light and the gold and the blue, and the little flies that made merry in the way, I took courage.

At the lower end of the wood, as you know, the path falls down steeply towards the stream, and when it has left the wood there are meadows to right and left, that were bright with yellow flowers at this time. In front the stream runs across the road under hazels, and where the chapel is still a-building over his body, on the left side, with its back against the wood stood his little house.

I will tell you of all this, as I saw it then; for the pilgrims have trampled it all about now, and the stream is all befouled and the banks broken, and the trees cut down by the masons that came to make the second chapel where Master Richard was wont to bathe himself, against the fiend's temptations at first, and afterwards for cleanness' sake, too—(for I never heard of a hermit as cleanly as was this young man, soon, and in spite of his washings, by the prayers of our Lady and saint Giles, to be declared among the blessed servants of God.)

The meadow was a fair circle of grass; with trees on every side but on this where the gate stood. It sloped to the stream that ran shallow over the stones, and down across it from the cell to the pool lay the path trampled hard by Master Richard's feet; for he had lived there four years at this time since his coming from Cambridge. Besides this path there was another that circled the meadow, and it was on this that he walked with God. I have seen him there sometimes from the gate, with his hands clasped, fingers to fingers, and his eyes open but seeing nothing; and if it had not been for the sin in my soul (on which God have pity!) I might have seen, too, the heavenly company that often went with him and of which he told me.

Before the hut lay a long garden-bed, in which the holy youth grew beans in their season, and other vegetables at other times; for it was on these, with nuts from the hazelwood, and grasses of which I know not the names (though he has told me of them many times), with water from the stream, that he sustained his life.

On either side of the hut stood a great maytree; it was on account of these that he had built his little house here, for he knew the properties and divine significations of such things.

The house itself was of wattles, plastered with mud from the brook, and thatched with straw. There was a door of wood that he leaned against the opening on this side when he prayed, but not when he slept, and a little square window high up upon the other side that looked into the green wood. It is of that same door that saint Giles' new altar was made, for the house fell down after his going, and the wind blew about the mud and the sticks, and the pilgrims have now carried all away. I took the door myself, when I came back and had seen him go through the heavenly door to our Lord.

The house within was a circle, three strides across, with a domed roof like a bee-hive as high as a man at the sides and half as high again in the centre. On the left lay his straw for a bed, and above it on the wall the little square of linen that he took afterwards with him to London, worked with the five precious wounds of our Saviour. On the right hand side was a wooden stool where he sat sometimes to pray and on the wall against it a little press that held some bottles within, and in another shelf some holy relics that are now in the church, and in another his six books; and above, upon the top, a little cross with our Lord upon it, very rude; for he said that the eyes of the soul should not be hindered by the eyes of the body, and that our Lord showed Himself often to him more clearly and truly than a craftsman could make Him. Above the window was a little figure of the Mother

14

of God, set there, he told me, above the sight of the green wood, because she was the mother of all living, and had restored what Eve had spoiled.

I cannot tell you, my children, of the peace of this place. The little house, and indeed the whole circle of the meadow set about with trees, was always to me as a mansion in paradise. There were no sounds here but the song of the birds and the running of the water and the wind in the trees; and no sight of any other world but this, except in winter when the hill over against the hut showed itself through the branches not three hundred paces away. On all other sides the woods rose to the sky. I think that the beasts knew the peace of the place. I have seen often a stag unafraid watching Master Richard as he dug or walked on his path; the robins would follow him, and the little furry creatures sit round him with ears on end. And he told me, too, that never since he had come to the place had blood fallen on the earth except his own when he scourged himself. The hunting-weasel never came here, though the conies were abundant; the stags never fought here, though there was a fair ground for a battlefield. It was a peace that passed understanding, and what that peace is the apostle tells us.

Here I came then on Corpus Christi evening, thirty

years ago, as the sun was near its setting behind the gate through which I came, and my shadow lay half-across the meadow before me.

It appeared to me that somewhat was amiss, but I knew not what it was: I was a little afraid. Master Richard was not to be seen, but his door was wide, so I thought he would not be praying. As I came up the path I saw something that astonished me. There was a circle of beasts about the hut, little conies that sat in the sunlight and shadow, without feeding, though it was the time for it; and as I came nearer I saw other beasts. There was a wild cat crouched in the shadow of the hazels moving his tail from side to side; a stag with his two does stood beneath a beech-tree, and a boar looked over the bank against which stood the hut.

They did not move as I came up and looked in at the door.

This is what I saw within.

The holy youth was seated on his stool with his hands gripping the sides and his eyes open, and he was looking towards the image of our Saviour on the right-hand side.

You have seen his holy and uncorrupt body, but in life he was different to that. He was not above twenty years old at this time, and of a beauty that drew men's eyes to him.* His hair was as you know it: a straight, tawny, nut-brown head of hair that fell to his shoulders; and he had the cleanest line of face that ever I have seen. His hair came low upon his straight forehead; his nose was straight, with fine nostrils; he had a little upper lip on which grew no hair, a full lip beneath very short, and a round cleft chin; his eyebrows were dark and arched; his whole face smooth and thin, and of an extraordinary clean paleness; he had a curved throat turned to a pale brown by the sun, though the colour of his body, I have heard it said, was as white as milk. He was dressed always in a white kirtle beneath, and a brown sleeveless frock over it of the colour of his hair, that came to his ankles, and was girt with a leather band. He went barefoot, but carried a great hat on his shoulders when he walked. He moved slowly at such times, and bore himself upright. His hands were fine and slender, and were burned brown like his face and his throat.

I tell you that I have never seen such a wonderful beauty in mortal man; and his soul was yet more lovely. It is no wonder that God's Majesty delighted in him, and that the saints came to walk with him. He was like neither man nor woman. He had the grey eyes of a woman, the mouth and chin of a man, the hands of a matron, and the

---

* This is the exact phrase used of Richard Rolle, hermit of Hampole.

figure of a strong virgin. I was always a little man, as you know, and when I walked with him, as I did sometimes, the top of my cap came just beneath his ear.

Master Richard, as I have said, was seated now on his stool, with his knees together, and his hands gripping the sides of his seat. His chin was a little thrust out, and he was as still as a stock. This I knew, was the manner in which sometimes he entered into strong contemplation; and I knew, too, that he would neither hear me nor see me till he moved. So I watched him a moment or two, and I grew yet more afraid as I watched; for this is what I saw:

Down from his temples across his cheeks ran little drops of sweat on to his brown frock, and that though it was a cool evening, and his spade was hung on its peg beneath the window. (It was the spade that you have seen in the church with a cross-handle polished by his holy hands.)

I looked for a while, and I grew yet more afraid. It seemed to me that there was somewhat in the cell that I could not see. I looked up at the window but there was nothing there but the still green hazel leaves; I looked at his bed, at the smooth mud walls and floor, at the domed roof, and, through the hole in the centre, where the smoke escaped when he made a fire, I could see leaves again and the evening sky. Yet the place was full of something; there was something of energy or conflict, I knew not which: some person was striving there.

Then I was suddenly so much afraid that I dared not stay, and I went back again along the path, and walked at the lower end of the meadow beside the stream.

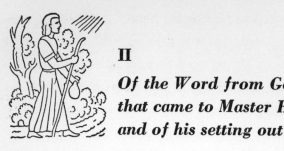

II

Of the Word from God that came to Master Hermit: and of his setting out

Vias tuas, Domine, demonstra mihi: et semitas tuas edoce me.

Shew, O Lord, Thy ways to me: and teach me Thy paths.
　　　　　　　　　　　　　　　　　　—Ps. xxiv. 4.

THERE are, as you have learned from me, and I from Master Richard Raynal, a trinity of natures in man. There is that by which he has to do with the things of matter—his five wits; that by which he has to do with God Almighty and the saints—his immortal soul and her powers; and, for the last, that by which he has to do with men—his lower understanding, his mind, his power of speech, and the like. Each nature has its proper end, though each ministers to the other. With his ears he hears God's Word, with his immortal soul he perceives God Almighty in what is seen with the eyes; with his understanding he comprehends the nature of flowers and the proper time to sow or reap. This trinity may be devoted to God or the fiend. . . . It is not true, as some have said, that it is only with the soul that God is perceived or served, and that the other two are unclean. We may serve God by digging with the hands, by talking friendly with our neighbour, and by the highest of all which is contemplation.

This is what Master Richard did, following the Victorines but not altogether. He strove to serve God alike in all, and I count his life, therefore, the highest that I have ever known. He said that to dig, to talk over the gate with a neighbour, and to contemplate the Divine Essence, were all alike to serve God. He counted none wasted, for God Almighty had made the trinity of natures in His own image, and intended, therefore, a proper occupation for each. To refuse to dig or to talk was not to honour contemplation; and this he said, though he said besides that some could not do this through reason of finding that one distracted the other. I count, however, that his own life was the hardest, for he did all three, and did not suffer one to distract another.

The most difficulty of such a life is to know when to follow one and when the other, when to dig, when to speak, and when to contemplate; and he would tell me that for this there are two guides that God Almighty sends—the one is that of exterior circumstance, and the other that of an interior knowledge, and he would follow that which cried the louder. If he desired to contemplate and a neighbour came to talk with him; if he perceived the neighbour clearly he would give over his contemplation; if not he would continue to contemplate. Again, if the imagination of a spade came mightily before him, or if he remembered that the sun would soon be up and his beans not watered, again he would give over his contemplation and dig or carry water.

For this there is needed one thing, and that a firm and quiet simplicity. He would do nothing till his mind was quiet. The friend of God must be as a little child, as the gospel tells us, and when the soul is quiet there is no difficulty in knowing what must be done. The first business then of a solitary's life is to preserve this quiet against the fiend's assaults and disquiet. And, I think, of all that I have ever known, Master Richard's soul was the most quiet, and most like to the soul of a little child.

As I walked now beside the stream I knew very well that it was for this that he was striving in contemplation: the sweat that ran down his cheeks was the sign of the fiend's assault, and I knew that I had done well to come. I had followed, as Master Richard himself had taught me, that loud interior voice.

So I strove to become quiet myself; I signed myself with the cross, and cried softly upon saint Giles to pray for me to God's Majesty that I might know what to say and do. Then I placed myself, as I had learned, at the divine feet; I looked at the yellow flowers and the clear running water and the open sky, and presently I was aware that all was silence within and without me. So I waited and walked softly to and fro, until Master Richard came to the door of his hut.

He stood there for a full minute, I suppose, with the sun on his face and his brown frock and broad white sleeves, before he saw me; for I was in the shadow of the hazels. Then he waved his hands a little and came slowly and very upright down the path in the middle, and as I went towards him I saw the beasts had gone. They were content, I suppose, now that their master was come out.

He came down the path, very pale and grave, and knelt as usual for my blessing, which I gave; then he kissed my skirt as he always did with a priest, and stood up.

Now I will try to tell you all that he said as he said it.

We went together without speaking, to the hut, and he brought out the stool into the sunlight and made me sit upon it, and sat himself upon the ground beneath me,

23

with his hands clasped about his knee, and his bare feet drawn beneath him. I could see no more of him but his brown hair and his throat, and his strong shoulders bent forward. Then he began to speak. His voice was always grave and steady.

"I am glad you are come, Sir John; I have something to ask you. I do not know what to do. I will tell you all."

I said nothing, for I knew what he wished; so I looked down across the meadow at the hazels and the pigeons that were coming down to the wood, and desired saint Giles to tell me what to say.

"It is this," he said. "Four days ago I was in contemplation, down there by the stream. The sensible warmth of which I have told you was in my heart; as it has been for over one year now, ever since I passed from the way of illumination. I think that it had never been so clear and strong. It was our Lord who was with me, and I perceived Him within as He always shows Himself to me; I cannot tell you what He is like, but there were roses on His hands and feet, and above His heart and about His head. I have not often perceived Him so clearly. His Mother, I knew, was a little distance away, behind me, and I wondered why it was so, and the divine John was with her. Then I understood that He was lonely, but no more than that; I did not know why. I said what I could,

24

and then I listened, but He said nothing to me, and then, after a while, I understood that it was under another aspect that He was there; that there was one in His place, crowned with gold instead of roses, and I could not understand it. I was astonished and troubled by that, and the warmth was not so strong at my heart.

"Then He was gone; and I saw the stream again beneath me, and the leaves overhead, and there was sweat on my forehead.

"When I stood up there was a knowledge in my heart —I do not know whether from our Lord or the fiend— that I must leave this place, and go to one whom I thought must be the King with some message; but I do not know the message."

My children, it was a dreadful thing to hear that. He had never spoken so since his coming four years before, except once when he was in the purgative way, and the fiend came to him under aspect of a woman. But he had been in agony then, and he was quiet now. Before I could speak he spoke again.

"I said that I could not go; that God Almighty had brought me here and caused me to build my house and given me the meadow and the water and the beasts as my friends—that I was neither monk nor friar nor priest

25

to be sent hither and thither—that I could not go. I cried on Him to help me and shew me His will; and then I went to dinner.

"Since that time, Sir John, the warmth has left me. I see the flowers, but there is nothing behind them; and the sunlight, but there is no heavenly colour in it. My mind is disquiet; I cannot rest nor contemplate as I should. I have been up the stairs that I have told you of a thousand times; I have set myself apart from the world, which is the first step, until all things visible have gone; then I have set myself apart from body and my understanding so that I was conscious of neither hands nor heart nor head, nor of aught but my naked soul; then I have left that, which is the third step; but the gate is always shut, and our Lord will not speak or answer. Tell me what I must do, Sir John. Is it true that this is from our Lord, and that I must go to see the King?"

I was sick at heart when I heard that, and I strove to silence what my soul told me must be my answer.

"It has persevered ever since, my son Richard?" I said.

He bowed his head.

"There is no savour in anything to me until I go," he answered. "This morning as I looked from over the wall upon the sacrament, my eyes were blinded: I saw nothing but the species of bread. I was forced to rest upon the assent of my faith."

Again I attempted to silence what my soul told me. It was the very power that Master Richard had taught me to use that was turning against what I desired. I had not known until then how much I loved this quiet holy lad with grave eyes—not until I thought I should lose him.

"There is no sin," I said, "that has darkened your eyes?"

I saw him smile sideways at that, and he turned his head a little.

"My sins are neither blacker nor whiter than they have always been," he said; "you know them all, my father."

"And you wish to leave us?" I cried.

He unclasped his hands and laid one on my knee. I was terrified at its purity, but his face was turned away, and he said nothing.

I had never heard the wood at that time of the evening so silent as it was then. It was the time when, as the lax monks say, the birds say mattins (but the strict observants call it compline), but there was neither mattins nor compline then in the green wood. It was all in a great hush, and the shadows from the trees fifty paces away had crept up and were at our feet.

Then he spoke again.

"Tell me what your soul tells you," he said.

I put my hand on his brown head; I could not speak. Then he rose at once, and stood smiling and looking on me, and the sunlight made a splendour in his hair, as it were his heavenly crown.

"Thank you, my father," he said, though I had not spoken one word.

Then he turned and went into the hut, and left me to look upon the green woods through my tears, and to listen to a mavis that had begun to sing in one of the may-trees. I knew he was gone to make ready.

The sun had quite gone down before he came out again, and the shadows were like a veil over the land; only the yellow flowers burned hot like candle flames before me.

He had four books in his hand and a little bottle, his hat on his shoulders, and the wooden sandals on his feet that he had worn to walk in four years before when he came to us. His little linen picture of the five wounds was fastened over his breast with thorns. He carried across his arm the second white-sleeved kirtle that he

had, and his burse was on his girdle. He held out two of
the books to me.

"These are for you, my father," he said; "the book
of hours and the *Regula Heremitarum* I shall take with
me, and all the rest of the mobills and the two other
books I shall leave at our Lord's disposal, except the
bottle of Quintessence."

I took the two books and looked at them.

There was Master Hoveden's *Philomela,* and a little
book he had made on Quinte Essence.

"But you will need them!" I cried.

"I carry *Philomela* in my heart," he said, "and as for
the Quinte Essence I shall have enough if I need it, and
here is the bottle that holds that that has been made of
blood.—The fifth—being of gold and silver I have not.
Argentum et aurum non est mihi."*

(That was the little bottle that I have told you of before. It was distilled of his own blood, according to the
method of Hermes Trismegistus.)

"If I do not return," he said, "I bequeath all to you;
and I wish six masses to be said; the first to be sung, of
Requiem; the second of the five wounds; the third of the
assumption; the fourth of all martyrs with a special
memory of saint Christopher; the fifth of all confessors

* "Silver and gold I have none." (Acts iii. 6.)

with a special memory of saint Anthony, hermit, and saint Giles, abbot; the sixth of all virgins with a special memory of saint Agnes."

You understand, my children, that he knew what would come to him, and that he had foreseen all; he spoke as simply as one who was going to another village only, looking away from me upon the ground. (I was glad of that.)

I begged of him to bid good-bye to his meadow.

"I will not;" he said, "I bear it with me wherever I go."

Then he took me by the arm, carrying his shod staff in his other hand, and led me to the gate, for I was so blinded that I stumbled as I went.

Once only did I speak as we passed upwards through the dark wood.

"And what will be your message," I asked, "when you come to the King?"

"Our Lord will tell it me when I come thither," he said.

We went through the village that lay dark and fast asleep. I wished him to go to some of the houses, and bid the folks good-bye, but he would not.

"I bear them, too, wherever I go," he said.

After we had adored God Almighty in the church,* and I had shriven the young man and blessed him, we went out and stood under the lychgate where his body afterwards rested.

It was a clear night of stars and as silent as was once heaven for the space of half-an-hour. The philomels had given over their singing near a month before, and it was not the season for stags to bray; and those, as you know, are the principal sounds that we hear at night.

We stood a long time listening to the silence. I knew well what was in my heart, and I knew presently what was in his. He was thinking on his soul.

He turned to me after a while, and I could see the clear pallour of his face and the line of his lips and eyes all set in his heavy hair.

"Do you know the tale of the Persian king, Sir John?"

I told him No; he had many of such tales. I do not know where he had read them.

"There was once a king who had the open eyes, and he looked into heaven and hell. He saw there two friends whom he had known in the flesh; the one was a hermit, and the other another king. The hermit was in hell, and the king in heaven. When he asked the reason of this,

* That is, God present in the Blessed Sacrament.

one told him that the hermit was in hell because of his consorting with the king, and the king in heaven because of his consorting with the hermit."

I understood him, but I said nothing.

"Pray for me then, Sir John," said Master Richard.

Then we kissed one another, and he was gone without another word along the white road.

III

*How Master Richard fared:
how he heard Mass in Saint
Pancras' Church: how he came
to Westminster: and of his
colloquy with the Ankret*

Abyssus abyssum invocat: in voce cataractarum tuarum.

Deep calleth on deep: at the noise of Thy flood-gates.—*Ps. xli.* 8.

THE tale of his journey and of his coming to London he told me when I saw him again at the end. He spoke to me for over an hour, and I think that I have remembered near every word, but I cannot write down the laughter and the tears that were in his voice as he told me.

As he went along the road beneath the trees and the stars, carrying his kirtle, with his books and other things in his burse, and his hat on his shoulders, he was both happy and sorry.

There are two kinds of happiness for mortal men: there is that which is carnal and imperfect and hangs on circumstances and the health of the body and such like things; and there is that which is spiritual and perfect,

33

which hangs on nothing else than the doing of the will
of God Almighty so far as it is known, so that a man
may have both at once, or either without the other. Master Richard had the one without the other.

At first he could not bear to think of what he had left
behind him—his little quiet house and meadow and the
stream where he washed, and the beasts and men that
loved him; and he threw himself upon the other happiness for strength. By the time that he had arrived at the
ford he was so much penetrated by this better joy that
he was able to look back, and tell himself, as he had told
me, that he bore with him always wherever he went all
that he had left behind him. It was ever his doctrine that
we lose nothing of what is good and sweet in the past,
and that we suck out of all things a kind of essence that
abides with us always, and that every soul that loves is
a treasure-house of all that she has ever loved. It is only
the souls that do not love that go empty in this world and
in saecula saeculorum. He thought much of this on his
road, and by the time that he had come so far that he
thought it best to sleep by the wayside, the warmth had
come back that had left him for four days.

He went aside then out of the road to find a hazel
thicket, and by the special guidance of God found one
with a may-tree beside it. There he groped together the

dead leaves, took off his burse and his hat and his girdle
and his brown habit, and laid the habit upon the leaves,
unpinning the five wounds, and fastening them again
upon his white kirtle. Then he knelt down by the may-
tree, and said his prayers, beginning as he always did:
*"Totiens glorior, quotiens nominis tui, JESU, re-
cordor."* *

Then he repeated the Name an hundred times, and
his heart grew so hot and the sweetness in his mouth so
piercing that he could scarce go on. Then he committed
himself to the tuition of the glorious Mother of Christ,
and to that of saint Christopher, saint Anthony, hermit,
and saint Agnes, virgin, and lastly to that of saint Giles
and saint Denis, remembering me. Then he said compline with *paternoster, avemaria,* and *credo,* signed himself with the cross, and lay down on his kirtle—*specialissimus,* darling of God—and drew the second kirtle over
his body for fear of the dews and the night vapours; and
so went to sleep, striving not to think of where he had
slept last night. (He told me all this, as I have told you.)

He awoke at dawn in an extraordinary sweetness
within and without, and as he walked in his white habit
beneath the solemn beech-trees, his soul opened wide to
salute the light that rose little by little, pouring down on

* "I glory, so often as I remember Thy Name, JESU."

him through the green roof. The air was like clear water, he said, running over stones, brightening without concealing their colours; and he drank it like wine. He had that morning in his contemplation what came to him very seldom, and I do not know if I can describe it, but he said it was the sense that the air he breathed was the essence of God, that ran shivering through his veins, and dropped like sweet myrrh from his fingers. There was the savour of it on his lips, piercing and delicate, and in his nostrils.

He set out a little later after he had washed, following the road, and came to a timber chapel standing by itself. I do not know which it is, but I think it must have been the church of saint Pancras that was burned down six years after. The door was locked, but he sat to wait, and after an hour came a priest in his gown to say mass. The priest looked at him, but answered nothing to his good-day (there be so many of these idle solitaries about that feign to serve God, but their heart is in the belly). I do not blame the priest; it may be he had been deceived often before.

There was a fellow who answered the mass, and Master Richard knelt by himself at the end of the church.

When mass was over the two others went out without a word, leaving him there. He said *ad sextam* then, and was setting out once more when the priest came back with a jug of ale and a piece of meat and bread which he offered him, telling him he would have given him nothing if he had begged.

Master Richard refused the meat and the ale, and took the bread.

The priest asked him his business, and he said he was for London to see the King.

The priest asked him whether he would speak with the King, and he told him Yes if our Lord willed.

"And what have you to say to him?" asked the priest.

"I do not know," said Master Richard.

The priest looked at him, and said something about a pair of fools, but Master Richard did not understand him then, for he had not heard yet the tale that the King was mad or near it.

So he kissed the priest's skirt, and asked his blessing; then he went down the steps to the little holy well (which makes me think it to be saint Pancras's church) and drank a little water after signing himself with it and commending himself to the saint, and went on his way. The sun was now high and hot, but he told me that when he looked back at the turn of the path the priest was at the gate in the full sun staring after him.

Of his journey that day there is not much to relate.

He went by unfrequented ways, walking sedately as his manner was, with devotion in his heart. An hour before noon a woman gave him dinner as she came back from taking it to her husband who burned charcoal in the forest, and asked him a kiss for payment when he had done his meal, sitting on a tree, with her standing by and looking upon him all the while. But he told her that he was a solitary, and that he had kissed no woman but his mother, who had died ten years before, so she appeared content, though she still looked upon him. Then as he stood up, thanking her for the dinner, she caught his hand and kissed that, and he reproved her gently and went on his way again.

For many miles after that it was the same; he saw no man, but only the beasts now and then, walking beneath the high branches in the sylvan twilight, over the dead leaves and the fern, and seeing now and again, as he expressly told me, for it seemed he had some lesson from it, the hot light that danced in the open spaces to right and left.

He saw one strange sight, which I should not have believed if he had not told me, and that was a ring of bulls in a clearing that tossed something this way and that, one to the other; he drove them off, and found that it was a hare, not yet dead, but it died in his hands. He told me that this verse came to his mind as he laid the poor beast down under a tree; *Circumdederunt me vituli multi: tauri pingues obsederunt me,** and there is no wonder in that, for it is from a psalm of the passion, and it was what befell him afterwards, as you shall hear.

Soon after that he bathed himself in a pool, for he was hot with walking, and desired to be at his ease when he saw folk again; and he dipped his sandals, too, to cool them.

Then he went in his white kirtle a little, until his hair was dried, and when the heat of the day began to turn he was aware that he was coming near to a village, for there was a herd of pigs that looked on him without fear.

The village was a very little one, but it stood upon a road, and here he had his first sight of the town-folks, for as he rested by a gate a company of fellows went by from the wars. I suppose that they were lately come from France (maybe from Arfleet),† for he told me that there were pavissors among them—the men with the great shields called pavices which are used only in sieges from the wooden castles that they push against the walls of the town. They were stained with travel, too, and were very silent and peevish. There were all sorts

* "Many calves have surrounded me: fat bulls have besieged me." (Ps. xxi. 13.)

† That is, Harfleur.

there besides the pavissors—the men-at-arms in their plate and mail-shirts, the archers in their body-armour and aprons, and the glaive-men* with the rest. He said that one company that rode in front had the sign of the Ragged Staff upon their breasts, by which he learned afterwards that they were my lord Warwick's† men.

One cried out to him to know how far was it to London, but he shook his head and said that he was a stranger. The fellow jeered and named him bumpkin, but the rest said nothing, and looked on him as they passed, and two at the end doffed their caps. They were about two hundred, and one rode in front with a banner borne before him; but it was a still hot day, and Master Richard could not see the device, for the folds hung about the staff.

He saw other folks after that here and there, although he avoided the villages where he could; but he got no supper, and an hour before sunset he came to the ferry over against Westminster. The wherries were drawn up on the beach, and he came down to these past Lambeth House, wondering how he was to get over.

He besought one man for the love of Jesu to take him

* Glaives were a kind of pike, but with long curved cutting-blades. Bills had straight blades.

† The Ragged Staff was the emblem of Lord Warwick.

40

over, but he would not; and another for the love of
Mary, and a third for the sake of the Rood of* Brom-
holm, and a fourth for the love of saint Anthony. And
at that they laughed at him, coming round him and looking on him curiously, and crying that they would have
all the saints out of him before *Avemaria,* and asking to
know his business. When he told them in his simplicity
that he was to see the King, they laughed the more, and
said that the King was gone to be a monk at saint Ed-
monds, and that he had best look for him there.

Then he asked yet another, a great fellow with a hairy
face and chest, to take him over for the love of saint
Denis and saint Giles, and the fellow swore a great oath,
elbowed his way out of the press that were all staring
and laughing, and bade him follow.

So he got into the boat and sat there while the man
carried down the oars, and all the rest crowded to look
and question and mock. He told me that he supposed at
the time that all the folks looked at him for that they
were not used to see solitaries, but I do not think it was
that. I tell you that one who looked a little on Master
Richard would look long, and that one who looked long
must either laugh or weep, so surprising was his beauty
and his simplicity.

* A famous relic of the True Cross.

When they were half-way over the fellow told him which was the abbey church, and Master Richard said that he knew it, for that he had seen it four years before when he came under our Lord's hand from Cambridge, and that he would ask shelter from the monks.

"And there is an ankret,* is there not?" asked Master Richard.

The man told him Yes, looking upon him curiously, and he told him, too, where was his cell. Then he put him on shore without a word save asking for his prayers.

I cannot tell you how Master Richard came to the ankret's cell, for I was only at Westminster once when Master Richard went to his reward, but he found his way there, marvelling at the filth of the ways, and looked in through the little window, drawing himself up to it by the strength of his arms.

It was all dark within, he told me, and a stench as of a kennel came up from the darkness.

He called out to the holy man, holding his nostrils with one hand, and with the other gripping the bars and sitting sideways on the sill of the window. He got no answer at first, and cried again.

---

* An ankret was a solitary, confined to one cell with episcopal ceremonies.

Then there came an answer.

There rose out of the darkness a face hung all over with hair and near as black as the hair, with red-rimmed eyes that oozed salt rheum. The holy man asked him what he wished, and why did he hold his nostrils.

"I wish to speak with your reverence," said Master Richard, "of high things. I hold my nostrils for that I cannot abide a stench."

The red eyes winked at that.

"I find no stench," said the holy man.

"For that you are the origin of its propagation," said Master Richard, "and dwell in the midst of it."

It was foolish, I think, of the sweet lad to speak like that, but he was an-angered that a man should live so. But the holy solitary was not an-angered.

"And in God's Majesty is the origin of my propagation," he said. *"Ergo."*

Master Richard could think of no seemly answer to that, and he desired, too, to speak of high matters; so he let it alone, and told the holy man his business, and where he lived.

"Tell me, my father," he said, "what is the message that I bear to the King. It may be that our Lord has revealed it to you: He has not yet revealed it to me."

"Are you willing to go dumb before the King?"

"I am willing if God will," said Master Richard.

"Are you willing that the King should be deaf and dumb to your message?"

"If God will," said Master Richard again.

"What is that which you bear on your breast?"

"It is the five wounds, my father."

"Tell me of your life. Are you yet in the way of perfection?"

Then the two solitaries talked together a long while; I could not understand all that Master Richard told to me; and I think there was much that he did not tell me, but it was of matters that I am scarce worthy to name, of open visions and desolations, and the darkness of the fourth Word of our Saviour on the rood; and again of scents and sounds and melodies such as those of which Master Rolle has written; and above all of charity and its degrees, for without charity all the rest is counted as dung.

Avemaria rang at sunset, but they did not hear it, and at the end the holy man within crept nearer and raised himself.

"I must see your face, brother," he said. "It may be then that I shall know the message that your soul bears to the King."

Master Richard came out of his heavenly swoon then,

and saw the face close to his own, and what he said of it to me I dare not tell you, but he bitterly reproached himself that he had ever doubted whether this were a man of God or no.

As he turned his own face this way and that, that the failing light might fall upon it, he said that beneath him in the little street there was a crowd assembled, all silent and watching the heavenly colloquy.

When he looked again, questioning, at the holy old man, he saw that the other's face was puckered with thought and that his lips pouted through the long-falling hair. Then it disappeared, and a grunting voice came out of the dark, but the sound of it was as if the old man wept.

"I do not know the message, brother. Our Lord has not shewed it to me, but He has shewed me this—that soon you will not need to wear His wounds. That is all I have to say. *Oremus pro invicem.*"*

The crowd pressed close upon Master Richard as he came down from the window, and, going in the midst of them in silence, he came to saint Peter's gate where the black monks dwell, and was admitted by the porter.

* "Let us pray for one another."

IV

How Master Richard saw the King in Westminster Hall: and of the Mass at Saint Edward's Altar

Revelabit condensa: et in templo ejus omnes dicent gloriam.

He will discover the thick woods: and in His temple all shall speak His glory.—*Ps. xxviii.* 9.

MASTER RICHARD did not tell me a great deal of his welcome in the monastery: I think that he was hardly treated and flouted, for the professed monks are not solitaries except those that be established in reputation; they call them self-willed and lawless and pretending to a sanctity that is none of theirs. Such as be under obedience think that virtue the highest of all and essential to the way of perfection. And I think, perhaps, they were encouraged in this by what had been said of themselves by our holy lord ten years before, for he was ever a favourer of monks.* But Master Richard did

* This may have been Eugenius IV., called *Gloriosus*. If so, it would fix the date of Richard at about 1444.

not blame them, so I will not, but I know that he was given no cell to be private in, but was sent to mix with the other guests in the common guest-house. I know not what happened there, but I think there was an uproar; there was a wound upon his head, the first wound that he received in the house of his friends, that I saw on him a little later, and he told me he had had it on his first coming to London. It was such a wound as a flung bone or billet of wood might make. He had now the *caput vulneratum*, as well as the *cor vulneratum** of the true lover of Jesus Christ.

He desired, after his simplicity, on the following morning, to speak with my lord abbot, but that could not be, and he only saw my lord at terce before mass, afar off sitting in his stall, a great prelate with his chain, and with one who bore a silver wand to go before him and do him service.

He prayed long in the church and at the shrine, and heard four or five masses, and saw the new grave of the Queen in the midst of the lady-chapel,† and did his devotions, hoping that our Lord would show him what to speak to the King, and then went to dinner, and after

* Wounded head . . . wounded heart.
† This may have been Queen Katharine, whose body was afterwards moved.

dinner set out to Westminster Hall, where he was told that the King could be seen that day.

He passed through the little streets that lay very nastily, no better than great gutters with all the filth of the houses poured out there, but he said that the folks there were yet more surprising, for these were they who had taken sanctuary here, and were dwelling round the monastery with their wives and children. There were all sorts there, slayers of men and deer, thieves, strikers of the clergy *suadente diabolo*,* false-coiners, harlots, and rioters; all under the defence of Religion, and not suffered to go out but on peril of being taken. He had a little company following him by the time that he came to the gate, some mocking and some silent, and all looking on him as he went.

When he came to the door of the hall the men that stood there would not let him in until he entreated them. They told him that the King was now going to dinner, and that the time was past, so he knew that it was not yet his hour to give the message that he knew not. But they let him in at last, and he stood in the crowd to see the King go by.

There was a great company there, and a vast deal of noise, for the audiences were done, and the bill-men

* "At the devil's persuasion"—a technical phrase.

were pushing the folks with their weapons to make room for the great men to go by, and the heralds were crying out. Master Richard stood as well as he could, but he was pushed and trampled about, and he could not see very well. They went by in great numbers; he saw their hats and caps and their furred shoulders between the crooked glaives that were gilded to do honour to the King, but there was such a crying out on all sides that he could not ask which was the King.

At last the shouting grew loud and then quiet, and men bowed down on all sides; and he saw the man whom he knew must be the King.

He had a long face (as I saw for myself afterwards), rather sallow, with a long straight nose and small, full mouth; his eyebrows were black and arched high, and beneath them his sorrowful eyes looked out on the people; he was bowing his head courteously as he came. On his head he wore a black peaked cap of velvet; there was ermine at his collar and a gold chain lay across his shoulders.

Now this is what Master Richard saw with the eyes of his body, but with the eyes of his soul he saw something so strange that I know not how to name or explain it.

He told me that it was our Saviour whom he saw go

by between the gilded glaives, as He was when He went from Herod's hall. I   do not understand how this may be. The King wore no beard as did our Saviour, he was full fourteen years younger at that time than was Jesu Christ when He suffered His bitter passion. They were of a height, I suppose, and perhaps the purple that the King wore was of the same colour as that which our Lord had put on him, but that was all the likeness that ever I could see, for the King's hair was black and his complexion sallow, but our Lord's was corn colour, and His face white and ruddy.* And, again, the one was but a holy man, and the other God Almighty although made man for our salvation.

Yet perhaps I did not understand Master Richard aright, and that he meant something else and that it was only to the eyes of the soul that the resemblance lay. If this is so, then I think I understand what it was that he saw, though I cannot explain it to you, any more than could he to me. There be some matters so high that no mouth can tell them, heart only can speak to heart, but I can tell you this, that Master Richard did not mean that our Lord was in the hall that day as He is in heaven

* A reference, I suppose, to Cant. Cant. v. 10.

and in the sacrament of the altar; it was something else
that he meant.* . . .

When Master Richard came out from the hall, he told
me that he was in a kind of swoon, but having his eyes
open, and that he knew not how he came back to the
guest-house. It was not until he knocked upon the door
that he saw that the crowd was about him again, staring
on him silently.

The porter was peevish as he pulled him in, and bade
him go and cut wood in the woodhouse for his keep, so
all that afternoon he toiled in his white kirtle at the cut-
ting with another fellow who cursed as he cut, but was
silent after a while.

Yet, when supper and bed-time came and Master
Richard had assisted at compline in the abbey-church,
still he knew not what the message was to be on Monday, when he would see the King and speak with him.

On Sunday he did no servile work, except that he
waited upon the guests, girt with an apron, and washed
the dishes afterwards. He heard four masses that day,
as well at all the hours, and prayed by himself a long
while at saint Edward's shrine, hearing the folks go by

* There follows a doctrinal disquisition.

to the tilting, and that night he went to bed with the servants, still ignorant of what he should say on the next day.

I am sure that he was not at all disquieted by his treatment, for he did not speak of it to me, except what was necessary, and he blamed no one. When I saw the porter afterwards he told me nothing except that Master Richard had worked well and willingly, and had asked for other tasks when his were done. He had asked, too, for a plenty of water to bathe himself, which he did not get. But whether he were disquieted or no on that Sunday, at least he was content next day, for it was on the next day at mass that our Lord told him what was the message that he was to deliver to the King.

There was a Cluniac monk from France who had obtained leave to say mass at the shrine of the Confessor, and Master Richard followed him and his fellow to the altar at five o'clock in the morning to hear mass there and see his Maker.*

He knelt down against the wall behind the high altar, and began to address himself to devotion, but he was distracted at first by the splendour of the tomb, the porphyry and the glass-work below, that Master Peter

* This is the common mediæval phrase. Men did not then bow their heads at the Elevation.

52

the Roman had made, and the precious shrine of gold above where the body lay, and the golden statues of the saints on either side. All about him, too, were such marvels that there is little wonder that he could not pray well for thinking on them—the kings that lay here and there and their effigies, and the paved steps on this side and that, and the fair painted glass and the high dark roof. Near where he knelt, too, he could see the great relic-chest, and knew what lay therein—the girdle of our Blessed Lady herself, mirror of chastity; the piece of stone marked by Christ's foot as He went up to heaven; a piece of the Very Rood on which He hanged; the precious blood that He shed there, in a crystal vase; the head of saint Benet, father of monks.* All these things have I seen, too, myself, so I know that they are truly there.

Behind him, as he kneeled on the stones, sounded the singing of the monks, and the noise of so much praise delighted him, but they ended soon, and at *Sanctus* his spirit began to be rapt into silence, and the holy things to make heaven about him.

He told me that he did not know what befell him until it came to the elevation of the sacring; only he knew that his soul was filled with lightness and joyousness, as when he had walked in the wood at dawn three days before.

* Surely not!

But as he lifted up his hands to see his God and to beat upon his breast, it appeared to him, he said, as if his feet rested again on some higher place: until then he had been neither on earth nor in heaven.

Now there was no visible imagination that came to him then; he said expressly that it was not so. There was none to be seen there but the priest in the vestment with his hood on his shoulders, and the *frater conversus** who held the skirt and shook the bell. Only it appeared to him that the priest held up the Body for a great space, and in that long time Master Richard understood many things that had been dark to him before. Of some of the things I have neither room nor wit to write; but they were such as these.

He understood how it was that souls might go to hell, and yet that it was good that they should go; how it was that our Saviour was born of His blessed Mother without any breaking of her virginity; how it is that all things subsist in God; in what manner it is that God comes into the species of the bread. But he could not tell me how these things were so, nor what it was that shewed him.†

* That is, the lay brother.

† There follow a few confused remarks on the relations of faith to spiritual sight.

There were two more things that were shewed him: the first, that he should not return home alive, but that his dead corpse should be carried there, and the second, what was the tidings that he should bear to the King.

Then he fell forward on his face, and so lay until the ending of the mass.

V

How Master Richard cried out in Westminster Hall: and of his coming to a Privy Parlour

Eructavit cor meum verbum bonum: dico ego opera mea regi.

My heart hath uttered a good word: I speak my works to the king.
—*Ps. xliv.* 1.

It would be about half an hour before the King's dinner-time, which was ten o'clock, that Master Richard came again to the hall.

There was not so great a press that day, and the holy youth was able to make his way near to the barrier that held back the common folk, and to see the King plainly. He was upon his seat beneath the cloth-of-estate that was quartered with the leopards and lilies, and had his hat upon his head. About him, beneath the scafford on which he sat were the great nobles, and my lord cardinal had a chair set for him upon the right-hand side, on the step below the King's.

All was very fair and fine, said Master Richard, with

56

pieces of rich stuff hanging upon the walls on this side and that beneath the windows, and, finest of all were the colours of the robes, and the steel and the gold and the white fur and the feathers, and the gilded glaives and trumpets, and coat-armour of the heralds.

There was a matter about to be concluded, but Master Richard could not tell what it was, for there was a din of talking all about him, and he saw many clerks and Religious very busy together in the crowd, shaking their fingers, lifting their brows, and clacking like rooks at sunset—so the young man related it. There were two fellows with their backs to him, standing in an open space before the scaffold with guards about them. One of the two was a clerk, and wore his square cap upon his head, and the other was not.

The King looked sick; he was but a young man at that time, not two years older than Master Richard. He was listening with his head down, to a clerk who whispered in his ear, kneeling by his side with papers and a great quill in his hand, and the King's eyes roved as he listened, now up, now down, and his fingers with rings upon them were arched at his ear. My lord cardinal had a ruddy face and bright holy eyes, and sat in his sanguine robes with his cap on his head, looking out with

57

his lips pursed at the clerks and monks that babbled to-gether beyond the barrier. He was an old man at this time, but wondrous strong and hearty.

At the end the King sat up, and there was a silence, but he spoke so low and quick, with his eyes cast down, and the shouting followed so hard upon his words, that Master Richard could not hear what was said. But it seemed to content the clerks and the Religious,* for they roared and clamoured and one flung up his cap so that it fell beyond the barrier and he could not come at it again. Then the two prisoners louted to the King, and went away with their guards about them; and the King stood up, and the cardinal.

Now this was the time on which Master Richard had determined for himself, but for a moment he could not cry out: it seemed as if the fiend had gripped him by the throat and were hammering in his bowels. The King turned to the steps, and at that sight Master Richard was enabled to speak.

He had not resolved what to say, but to leave that to what God should put in his mouth, and this is what he cried, in a voice that all could hear.

"News from our Lord! News from our Lord, your grace."

* King Henry VI. was a great favourer of ecclesiastics.

He said that when he cried that, there was first silence, and then such a clamour as he had never heard nor thought to hear. He was pushed this way and that; one tore at his shoulder from behind; one struck him on the head; he heard himself named madman, feeble-wit, knave, fond fellow. The guards in front turned themselves about, and made as though they would run at the crowd with their weapons, and at that the men left off heaving at Master Richard, and went back, babbling and crying out.

Then he cried out again with all his might.

"I bring tidings from my Lord God to my lord the King," and went forward to the barrier, still looking at the King who had turned and looked back at him with sick, troubled eyes, not knowing what to do.

A fellow seized Master Richard by the throat and pulled him against the barrier, menacing him with his glaive, but the King said something, raising his hand, and there fell a silence.

"What is your business, sir?" asked the King.

The fellow released Master Richard and stood aside.

"I bring tidings from our Lord," said the young man. He was all out of breath, he told me, with the pushing and striking, and held on to the red-painted barrier with both hands.

The king stooped and whispered with the cardinal, who was plucking him by the sleeve, for the space of a *paternoster,* and the murmuring began to break out again. Then he turned, and lifted his hand once more for silence.

"What are the tidings, sir?"

"They are for your private ear, your grace."

"Nay," said the King, "we have no private ear but for God's Word."

"This is God's Word," said Master Richard.

There was laughter at that, and the crowd came nearer again, but the King did not laugh. He stood still, looking this way and that, now on Master Richard, and now on the cardinal, who was pulling again at his sleeve. It seemed as if he could not determine what to do.

Then he spoke again.

"Who are you, sir?"

"I am a solitary, named Richard Raynal," said the young man. "I come from the country, from . . .* Sir John Chaldfield, the parson, will undertake for me, your grace."

"Is Sir John here?" asked my lord cardinal, smiling at the clerks.

* It is most annoying that the name of the village is wanting.

60

"No, my lord," said Master Richard, "he has his sheep in the wilderness. He cannot run about to Court."

There was again a noise of laughter and dissent from the crowd of clerks, and my lord cardinal smiled more than ever, shewing his white teeth in the midst of his ruddy face.

"This is a witty fellow, your grace," said my lord cardinal aloud to the King. "Will your grace be pleased to hear him in private?"

The King looked at Master Richard again, as if he knew not what to do.

"Will you not tell us here, sir?" he asked.

"I will not, your grace."

"Have you weapons upon you?" said my lord cardinal, still smiling.

Master Richard pointed to the linen upon his breast.

"I bear wounds, not weapons," he answered; which was a brave and shrewd answer, and one that would please the King.

His grace smiled a little at that, but the smile passed again like the sunshine between clouds on a dark and windy day, and the crowd crept up nearer, so that Master Richard could feel hot breath upon his bare neck behind. He committed his soul again to our Lady's tuition, for he knew not what might be the end if he were not heard out.

Well, the end of it was as you know. It was not possible for any man with a heart in his body to look long upon Master Richard and not love him, and the King's face grew softer as he looked upon that fair young man with his nut-brown hair and the clear pallour of his face and his pure simple eyes, and then at the coarse red faces behind him that crept up like devils after holy Job. It was not hard to know which was in the right, and besides the brave words that had stung the clerks to anger had stung the King to pity and pleasure; so the end was that the guards were bidden to let Master Richard through, and that he was to follow on in the procession, and be gently treated, and admitted to see the King when dinner was done.

So that, my children, is the manner in which it came about that my name was cried aloud before the King's presence, and the cardinals and the nobles, in Westminster Hall on the Monday after *Deus qui nobis.**

* So the collect of Corpus Christi begins. It was a common method, even among the laity, of defining dates.

VI

Of Master Richard's speaking with the King's Grace: and how he was taken for it

Et nunc reges intelligite: erudimini qui judicatis terram.

And now, O ye kings, understand: receive instruction, ye that judge the earth.—*Ps. ii.* 10.

THEY searched Master Richard for weapons, in spite of what he had said, when they had him alone in a little chamber off the King's closet, but not unkindly, after what had been ordered, but they found nothing beneath the white kirtle save the white skin, and nothing in the burse but the book of hours and a little pen-knife, and the bottle of Quinte Essence. One of them held that up, and demanded what it was.

"That is the cordial called Quinte Essence," said Master Richard, smiling.

They thought it to be a poison, so he was forced to explain that it was not.

"It is made from man's blood," he said, "which is

the most perfect part of our being, and does miracles if it is used aright."

They would know more than that, so he told them how it was made, with salt, and set in the body of a horse, and afterwards distilled, and he told them what marvels it wrought by God's grace; how it would draw out the virtues and properties of things, and could be mixed with medicines, and the rest, as I have told to you before. That is the bottle you have seen at the parsonage.

But they would not give it back to him at that time, and said that he should have it when the King had done talking with him. Then they went out and left him alone, but one stood at the door to keep him until dinner was over.

It was a little room, Master Richard said, and looked on to the river. It was hung with green saye, and was laid with rushes. There was a round table in the midst of the floor, and a chair on this side and that; and there was an image of Christ upon the rood that stood upon the table. There was another door than that through which he had been brought from the hall.

Master Richard, when he was left alone, tried to compose himself to devotion, but he was too much distracted by all that he had seen, until he had said *ad sextam,* and then he was quieter, and sat down before the table, looking upon the rood, and he did not know how long had passed before the King came in.

My children, I like to think of Master Richard then; it was his last peaceful hour that he spent until near the end when I came to him. But the peace of his heart did not leave him (except at one time), in spite of all that happened to him, for he told me so himself. Yet, save for the little wound upon his head, he was clean of all injury at this time, and I like to think of him in his strength and loveliness as he was then, content to give his tidings from our Lord to the King, and to abide what was to follow.

As the clock beat eleven, the King came suddenly through from his parlour, but he was not alone: my lord cardinal was with him.

As Master Richard knelt down on the floor to do them homage, he observed the King's dress: it was not as that of the other great men, for the King loved plain dress, and folks said that the clothing he would have liked best to wear was a monk's cowl or a friar's frock (and I doubt not that there be many a monk and friar, and clerk too, who would have been glad to change with him, for not every Religious man has a Religious heart!)...*

* There follows a little sermon on Vocation.

The King's dress was a plain doublet with a collar of ermine, and over it a cloak of royal purple lined and trimmed with fur, but cut very plainly with a round cape such as priests wear. He had the collar of *Sanctus Spiritus* over his shoulders, his cap on his head, with a peak to it, and little plain round shoes (not like those pointed follies that some wear, and that make a man's foot twice as long as God made it by His wisdom). My lord cardinal was in his proper dress, and bore himself very stately.

The King bade Master Richard stand up, and himself and my lord sat down in the two chairs beside one another, so that half their faces were in shadow and half in light. Master Richard saw again that the King looked somewhat sick, and very melancholy.

Then the King addressed himself to Master Richard, speaking softly, but with an appearance of observing him very closely. My lord, too, watched him, folding his hands in his lap.

"Now tell me, sir," said the King, "what is this tidings that you bear?"

Master Richard was a little dismayed at my lord's coming: he had thought it was to be in private.

"It was to your ear alone, your grace, that I was bidden to deliver the message," he said.

"My lord here is ears and eyes to me," said the King, a little stiffly, and my lord smiled to hear him, and laid his hand on the King's knee.

That was answer enough for the holy youth, who was attendant only for God's will; so he began straightway, and told the King of his contemplation of eight days before, and of the dryness that fell on him when he strove to put away his thoughts, and of his words with me who was his priest, and his coming to London and all the rest. Then he told him of how he heard mass at saint Edward's altar, and how at the elevation of the sacring our Lord had told him what tidings he was to take.

The King observed him very closely, leaning his head on his hand and his elbow on the table, and my lord, who had begun by playing with his chain, ceased, and watched him too.

Master Richard told me that there was a great silence everywhere when he had come to the matter of saint Edward's altar; it was such an exterior silence as is the interior silence that came to him in contemplation. There appeared no movement anywhere, neither in the room, nor the palace, nor the world, nor in the three hearts that were beating there. There was only the great presence of God's Majesty enfolding all.

When he ceased speaking, the King stared on him for

a full minute without any words, then he took his arm off the table and clasped his hands.

"And what was it that our Lord said to you, sir?" he asked softly, and leaned forward to listen.

Master Richard looked on the sick eyes, and then at the ruddy prelate's face that seemed very stern beside it. But he dared not be silent now.

"It is this, your grace, that our Lord shewed to me," he began slowly, "that your grace is not as other men are, neither in soul nor in life. You walk apart from all, even as our Saviour Christ did, when He was upon earth. When you speak, men do not understand you; they take it amiss. They would have you make your kingdom to be of this world, and God will not have it so. *Regnum Dei intra te est.** It is that kingdom which shall be yours. But to gain that kingdom you must suffer a passion, such as that which Jesu suffered, and this is the tidings that He sends to you. He bids you make ready for it. It shall be a longer passion than His, but I know not how long. Yet you must not go apart, as you desire. You must go this way and that at all men's will, ever within you *portans stigmata Domini Jesu.†* And the end of it shall be even as His, and as His apostles was who now rules

* "The kingdom of God is within thee" (from Luke xvii. 21).
† "Bearing the marks of the Lord Jesu" (from Gal. vi. 17).

68

Christendom. *Cum senueris, extendes manus tuas, et alius te cinget, et ducet quo tu non vis.** And when you come before the heavenly glory, and the blessed saints shall ask you of your wounds, you shall answer them as our Lord answered, *"His plagatus sum in domo eorum qui diligebant me."*†

When Master Richard had finished speaking, his head and body shook so much that he could scarce stand, or see the King plainly, and by this he perceived for a certainty that God was speaking by him. But he was aware that my lord cardinal was standing up with his hand outstretched and an appearance of great anger on his face. For indeed those were terrible things that Master Richard had said—that he should foretell the King's death in this manner, and all the sorrows that he should go through, for, as you know, all these words came about.

Yet it seemed that something restrained my lord from speaking till the other was done; but when Master Richard went back a step, shaking under the spirit of God, my lord burst out into words.

* "When thou shalt be old thou shalt stretch forth thy hands; and another shall gird thee, and lead thee whither thou wouldst not" (John xxi. 18).

† "With these I was wounded in the house of them that loved me" (Zack. xiii. 6).

Master Richard could not understand him; there was drumming in his ears, and the sweat poured from him, but when sight came back he observed my lord's face, red with passion, turning now to him, now to the King, who sat still in his place; his white eyebrows went up and down, and his scarlet cape and his rochet flapped this way and that as he shook his arms and cried out.

When he had done there was silence again for a full minute. Master Richard could hear the breathing of one in the gallery without.

Then the King rose up without speaking, but looking intently upon the young man, and still without speaking, went out from the room, and my lord went after him.

When Master Richard had stood a little while waiting, and there was no sound (for the door into the King's parlour was now shut again), he turned to the other door to go out; for he had delivered his message, and there was no more to be said.

The man that kept the door, and whose breathing Master Richard had heard just now, barred the way, and asked him his business.

"My business is done," said Master Richard, "I must go home again."

"And the King?" asked the fellow.

"The King and my lord are gone back into the parlour."

There was no cause to keep Master Richard any longer, so the fellow let him past, and he went down the gallery and the stairs towards the court that opened upon the hall.

But before he reached the door, there was a great tumult overhead, and a noise of men moving and crying, and Master Richard stayed to listen. (I had almost said that it had been better if he had not stayed, but made his way out quickly and escaped perhaps; but it is not so, as I now believe, for our Lord had determined what should be the end.)

Two fellows came running presently down the stairs up which Master Richard was looking. One of them was a page of my lord's, a lad dressed all in purple with the pointed shoes of which I have written before, and the other the man-at-arms that had kept the door. The lad cried out shrilly when he saw him standing there, and came down the steps four at a leap, with his hands outstretched to either wall. Master Richard thought that he would fall, and stepped forward to catch him, but the lad recovered himself on the rushes, and then, screaming with anger, sprang at the young man's throat, seizing it with one hand, and striking him in the face again and again with the other.

For an instant Master Richard stood amazed, then he caught the lad's hands without a word and held them so, looking at the man-at-arms who was now half-way down the stairs in his plate and mail, and at others who were following as swiftly as they could. In the court outside, too, there were footsteps and the sound of talking, and presently the door was darkened by half a dozen others, who ran up at the tumult, and all in a moment Master Richard found himself caught from behind and his hands pulled away, so that the lad was able to strike him again, which he did, three or four times.

So he was taken by the men and held.

Master Richard could not understand what the matter was, as he looked at the press that gathered every moment on the stairs and in the court. So he asked one that held him, and the page screamed out his answer above the tumult of voices and weapons.

So Master Richard understood, and went upstairs under guard, with the blood staining his brown and white dress, and his face bruised and torn, to await when the King should come out of the fit into which he had fallen, and judge him for the message which he had brought.

VII

Of Master Richard's Second speaking with his Grace: and of his detention

---

Abscondes eos in abscondito faciei tuae: a conturbatione hominum.

Thou shalt hide them in the secret of Thy face: from the disturbance of men.—*Ps. xxx.* 21.

I SCARCELY have the heart to write down all that befell Master Richard; and yet what it pleased God's Majesty that he should suffer, cannot displease Him to write down nor to think upon.* . . .

Master Richard was taken back again by two of the men-at-arms into the parlour where he had lately seen the King, and was allowed to stand by the window, looking out upon the river, while one fellow kept one door, and one the other.

He strove to keep quiet interiorly, keeping his eyes fixed upon the broad river in the sunshine and the trees

* There follows a curiously modern discussion on what I may call the gospel of Pleasure, which is a very different thing from the gospel of Joy. The former, as Sir John points out, disregards and avoids pain, the latter deals with it. He points out acutely that this difference is the characteristic difference between Greek and Christian philosophy.

on the other side, and his heart established on God's Will. He did not know then what kind of a fit it was into which the King had fallen, nor why it was that himself should be blamed for it; and when he spoke to the men they gave him nothing but black looks, and one blessed himself repeatedly, with his lips moving.

There came the sound of talking from the inner room, and once or twice the sound of glass on glass. Without it was a fair day, very hot and with no clouds.

Master Richard told me that he had no fear, neither now nor afterwards; it seemed to him as if all had been done before; he said it was as if he were one in a play, whose part and words are all assigned beforehand, as well as the parts and words of the others, by the will of the writer; so that when violence is done, or injustice, or hard words spoken, or death suffered, it is all part of the agreed plan and must not be resisted nor questioned, else all will be spoiled. It appeared to him too as if the ankret in the cell were privy to it all, and were standing, observing and approving; for Master Richard remembered what the holy man had said as to the five wounds marked upon the linen, and how he would not need to wear them much longer.

After about half-an-hour, as he supposed, the voices

waxed louder in the other room; and presently one came out from it in the black dress of a physician. He was a pale man, shaven clean, a little bald, and very thin. It was that physician that died last year.

He said nothing, though his face worked, and he beckoned sharply to Master Richard.

Master Richard went immediately across the floor and through into the further room.

There were a dozen persons gathered there, all staring upon the King, who sat in a great chair by the table. Two or three of these were servants, and the rest of them, with my lord cardinal, the nobles that had been in the palace at the time of the King's seizure. My lord cardinal was standing by the chair, very stern and anxious-looking; and all turned their faces, and there was an angry whisper from their mouths, as the young man came forward and halted; and the physician shut to the door.

But Master Richard did not observe them closely at that time; for he was looking upon the King.

The King sat very upright in his chair; his hands rested on the carved arms; and his face and eyes were as if made of Caen stone, chalky and hard. He was looking out from the room, Master Richard said; and Master Richard knew at once what it was that he was seeing.

It was that of which the holy youth had spoken; and was nothing else than the passion and death that came upon him afterwards. The words that the King had heard had opened the eyes of his soul, and he was now seeing for himself.

Before that any could speak or hinder, Master Richard was on his knees by the King, and had laid his lips to the white right-hand, seeing as he did so the red ring on the first finger. My lord cardinal sprang forward to tear him off, but the King turned his stony eyes; and my lord fell back.

Then Master Richard knew that he had not given the whole message; and that our Lord had not intended it at first. The message of the passion and death was to be first; and the second, second—first the wound, and then the balm.

So he began to speak; and these were the words as he told them to me.

"My lord King," he said, "Our Lord does not leave us comfortless when He sends us sorrow. This is a great honour, greater than the crown that you bear, to bear the crown of thorns. That bitter passion of Christ that He bore for our salvation is wrought out in the Body which is His Church, and especially in those members,

76

which, like his sacred hands and feet, receive the nails into themselves. Happy are those members that receive the nails; they are the more honourable; it was on His feet that He went about to do good; and with His hands that He healed and blessed and gave His precious body; and with His burning heart that He loves us.

"My lord King, men will name you fool and madman and crowned calf; it is to their shame that they do so, and to your honour. For so they named our Saviour. All who set not their minds on this world are accounted fools; but who will be the merrier in the world that is to come?

"And, last, our Lord has bestowed on your highness an honour that He bestows upon few, but which Himself suffered; and that, the knowledge of what is to be. In this manner the passion is borne a thousand times a day, by foreknowledge; and for every such pain there is a joy awarded. It is for this reason that you may bear yourself rightly, and that He may crown you more rich-ly that our Lord has sent me to you, and bidden me tell you this."

All this while Master Richard was looking upon the King's face, but there was no alteration in his aspect.

It was as the colour of ashes, and his eyes like stone; and yet Master Richard knew very well that his grace heard what was said, but could not answer it. (It was so with him often afterwards: he would sit thus without speaking or answering what was said to him: he would go thus to mass and dinner and to bed, as pale as a spirit: he would even ride thus among his army, with his crown on his head, and his sword in his hand, dumb but not deaf; and looking upon what others could not see: and all, as those about him knew very well, began from the hearing of the message that Master Richard Raynal brought to him from God's Majesty.)

While Master Richard was speaking the rest kept silence: for I think that somewhat held them for pity of those two young men—for the one that sat in such stiff agony, and for the other near as pale, and red with his own blood, that spoke so eloquently. But when he had done and had kissed the white hand again, my lord cardinal came forward, pushed him aside, and himself began to speak in a voice that was at once pitiful and angry, crying upon the King to answer, telling him that he was bewitched and under the power of Satan through the machinations of Master Richard, and blessing him again and again.

Master Richard stood aside watching, and wondering

that my lord could speak so, and not understand the
truth; and he looked round at the others to see if any
there understood. But they were all dumb, except for
muttering, and gave him black looks, and blessed themselves as their eyes met his; so he committed himself to
prayer.*

It was of no avail; the King could not speak; and
presently the physician, Master Blytchett,† came and
whispered in my lord's ear as he knelt at the King's
knees. My lord turned his head and nodded, and Master
Richard was seized from behind and pulled through the
door. The man who had pulled him was one of the servants. I saw him afterwards and spoke with him, when he
was sorry for what he had done; but now he spat on
Master Richard fiercely, for the door was shut; and
blessed himself mightily meanwhile.

Then he spoke to the man that kept the door; and said
that Master Richard was to be taken down and kept
close, until there was need of him again; for that the
King was no better.

So Master Richard was brought downstairs, and

* Sir John preaches a little sermon here on internal recollection, and
the advantages of the practice.

† This is an extraordinary name, and is obviously a corruption of some
English name, but I do not know what it can be, nor why it was retained,
when all others were erased.

through the guard-room into one of the little cells: and as he went he was thinking on the words of our Saviour.

*Si male locutus sum, testimonium perhibe de malo: si autem bene, quid me caedis?**

* "If I have spoken ill, give testimony of the evil, but if well, why strikest thou me?" (John xviii. 23).

VIII
Of the Parson's Disquisition on the whole matter

In columna nubis loquebatur ad eos.

He spoke to them in the pillar of the cloud.—*Ps. xcviii.* 7.

      At this point of the narrative, in consideration of what has preceded and what is yet to follow, Sir John Chaldfield *thinks it proper to enlarge at great length upon the threefold nature of man, and the various characters and functions that emerge from the developement of each part.*

      For the sake of those who are more interested in the adventures of Master Richard *and the King than in a medieval priest's surmises as to their respective psychological states, I shall take leave to summarize a few of his remarks and omit the rest. The whole section, in fact, might be omitted without any detriment to the history; and may be ignored by those who have arrived as far as this point in the reading of the book.*

Sir John *is somewhat obscure; and I suspect that he does not fully understand the theory that he attempts to state, which I suppose was taught him originally by* Richard Raynal *himself, and subsequently illustrated by the priest's own studies. He instances several cases as examples of the classes of persons to which he refers; but his obscurity is further deepened by the action of the zealous and discreet scribe, who, as I have said in the preface, has been careful to omit nearly all the names in* Sir John's *original manuscript.*

Briefly, his theory is as follows—at least so far as I can understand him.

It is at once man's glory and penalty that he is a mixed being. By the possession of his complex nature he is capable of both height and depth. He can devote himself to God or Satan; and there are two methods by which he can attain to proficiency in either of those services. He can issue forth through his highest or lowest self, according to his own will and predispositions.

Most men are predisposed to act through the lower or physical self; and by an interior intention direct their actions towards good or evil. Those that serve God in this manner are often incapable of high mystical acts: but

*they refrain generally from sin; and when they sin re-
turn through Penance. Those who so serve Satan sin
freely, and make no efforts at reformation. A few of
these, by a wholehearted devotion to evil, succeed in
establishing a relation between themselves and physical
nature, and gain a certain control over the lower powers
inherent in it. To this class belong the less important
magicians and witches; and even some good Christians
possess such powers (which we now call psychical) which,
generally speaking, they are at a loss to understand.
Such persons can blast or wither by the eye; they have
a strange authority over animals;* and are able to set
up a connection between inanimate material objects and
organic beings.† But such magic, even when malevolent,
need not be greatly feared by Christian men living in
grace: its physical or psychical influence can be counter-
acted by corresponding physical acts: such things as the
sign of the cross, the use of sacramentals, the avoidance*

---

* I append a form of words which Sir John quotes, and which, he says,
may be used sometimes lawfully even by christened men. It is to be addressed in necessity to a troublesome snake. "By Him who created thee I
adjure thee that thou remain in the spot where thou art, whether it be thy
will to do so or otherwise. And I curse thee with the curse wherewith the
Lord hath cursed thee."

† He instances the wasting of an enemy by melting a representation of
him fashioned in wax.

of notoriously injuriously follies such as beginning work on Friday, the observance of such matters as wearing Principium Evangelii secundum Joannem *on the person, and the paying of ocular deference to Saint Christopher on rising—these precautions and others like them are usually a sufficient safeguard.**

But all this is a very different matter from the high mysticism of contemplatives, ascetics, and Satanic adepts.

These are persons endowed with extraordinary dispositions, who have resolved to deal with invisible things through the highest faculty of their nature. The Satanic adepts are greatly to be feared, even in matters pertaining to salvation, for, although their power has been vastly restricted by the union of the divine and human natures in the Incarnation of the Son of God, yet they are capable by the exercise of their power, of obscuring spiritual faculties, and bringing to bear grievous temptations, as well as of afflicting by sickness, misfortune and death. These select souls are the great mages of all time; and their leader, since the year of redemption,

* I am afraid it is impossible to clear Sir John wholly of the charge of superstition. The "Beginning of the Gospel according to John" was the fourteen verses read as the last Gospel after mass. A copy of this passage was often carried, sewn into the clothes, to protect from various ills. The image of St. Christopher usually stood near the door of the church to ensure against violent death all who looked on it in the morning.

Simon Magus himself, could be dealt with by none other than the Vicar of Christ and prince of apostles.

It is not every man, even with the worst will in the world, who is capable of rising to this sinister position: for it is not enough to renounce the faith, to make a league with Satan, to insult the cross and commit other enormities: there must also be resident in the aspirant a peculiar faculty, corresponding to, if not identical with, the glorious endowment of the contemplative. If, however, all these and other conditions are fulfilled, the initiated person is severed finally from the Body of Christ and incorporated into that of Satan, through which mysterious regeneration it receives supernatural powers corresponding to those of the baptized soul.

Finally, Sir John *considers those whom he calls "God's adepts," and among those, though in different classes, he places* Richard Raynal *and the King.* These adepts, he says, are of every condition and character, but that which binds them together is the fact that they all alike deal directly with invisible things, and not, as others do, through veils and symbols. Since the Incarnation, however, all baptized persons who frequent the sacraments are in a certain degree adepts, for in those*

* A little later on he also mentions King Solomon as an eminent pre-Christian adept, and Enoch.

sacraments they may be truly said to see, handle, hear and taste the Word of Life. Other powers, however, are still reserved to those who are the masters of the spiritual life;—for not all persons, however holy, are contemplatives, ecstatics, or seers.

Now contemplation is an arduous labour; it is not, as some ignorant persons think, a process of idle absorption; it is rather a state of strenuous endeavour, aided at any rate in its first stages by acts of steady detachment from the world of sense. Richard Raynal had passed through the first rigour of that purgative stage in the short period of one year, and although he still lived a detached life, and practised various austerities, he was so far free of danger that he was able, as has been already remarked, to dig and talk without interrupting the exercise of his higher faculties. He had then passed to the illuminative stage, and had remained, again for one year, in the process of being informed, taught and kindled in preparation for the third and last stage of union with the Divine—elsewhere named the Way of Perfection. He had been rewarded by various sensible gifts, particularly by that of Ecstasy, by which the soul passes, as fully as an embodied soul can pass, into the state of eternity. Here mysteries are seen plainly, though they seldom can be declared in words, or at least only haltingly and under physical images that are not really adequate to that which they represent.*

With the King, however, it was different. By the exigencies of his vocation he was unable to live the properly contemplative life; solitude, an essential to that life, was impossible to him: but he had done what he could by asceticism and the habit of recollection; and further, his soul had been naturally one of those which had the necessary endowments of the contemplative.

The purgative, illuminative and unitive stages had therefore been confused, and had come upon him simultaneously, though gradually; and this as was to be expected, had resulted in intense suffering. There was for him no graduation by which he passed slowly upwards from detachment to union. Richard Raynal's words to him had coincided with the struggling emergence of his own soul on to the higher plane; and he had opened his spiritual eyes on to a terrible future for which he had but little preparation. The result had been a kind of paralysis of his whole nature, and henceforward the rest of his life, Sir John maintains, had been darkened by his first definite experience in the mystical region. If indeed this King was none other than Henry the Sixth, Sir John's

* That which Richard calls *Calor*, or Warmth, appears to be one of these.

explanation is an interesting commentary on that melancholy personage. Richard *then, according to this hypothesis, found joy in his contemplation because he had been trained to look for it; and* Henry *had found sorrow because he had been overwhelmed by the suddenness of the revelation and his own unpreparedness.* Sir John *adds that it is difficult to know which of the two lives would be more pleasing to God Almighty.*

As regards his whole statement I feel it is impossible to say more than to quote the opinion of a modern mystic to whom I submitted the original; which was to the effect that it contains a little nonsense, a good deal of truth, and a not intolerable admixture of superstition. He added further that Sir John *must not be judged hardly; for he was limited by an inadequate vocabulary and an ignorance of many of the terms that his scanty reading enabled him to employ.*

IX

How Master Richard took his meat: and of Master Lieutenant's whipping of him

Domine, ante te omne desiderium meum: et gemitus meus a te non est absconditus.

Lord, all my desire is before Thee: and my groaning is not hidden from Thee.—*Ps. xxxvii.* 10.

IT was a little cell in which Master Richard found himself that afternoon, after he had passed through the guardroom and heard the anger and laughter of the men-at-arms, and sustained their blows, and when he had looked about it, at the little narrow window high up upon the wall, and the water that dripped here and there from the stones, and the strong door shut upon him, the first thing that he did was to go down upon his knees in the puddle, and thank God for solitude.

(There be two kinds of men in the world, those that love solitude, and those that hate it; for there be two

89

kinds of souls, the full and the empty. Those that be full have enough to occupy them with, and those that be empty are for ever seeking somewhat wherewith to occupy them.)

When he had done that he looked round again upon the walls and the ceiling and the floor, and sitting down upon the wood that was to be his pillow, first girding up his kirtle that it might not be fouled, he sought to unite himself with all that he saw, that it might be his friend and not his foe. So he told me when I asked him, but I do not know if I understood him aright.

There he sat then a great while, communing with God, and the saints, with his cell and with his soul, and after a little time his interior quiet was again restored. Then, as he knew he would have no light that night, and that the cell would grow dark early, for his window looked eastwards, and was a very little one, he made haste to say the rest of his office from the book that he had with him. But he said it slowly, as the Carthusians use, sucking the sweetness out of every word, and saying *Jesu* or *Mary* at every star,* and after a while the sweetness was so piercing that he could scarcely refrain from crying out.

When he had done he looked again at his window, and

* The break in each verse of the psalter is marked with an asterisk.

saw that the strip of sky was becoming green with evening light, and he thought upon his hazels at home.

Half an hour afterwards a fellow came with his bread and water for supper, on a wooden plate and in a great jug, set them down and went out without speaking.

Now I will tell you all that Master Richard did; it was his custom when he was at home, and he observed it here too.

He first poured water upon his hands, saying the psalm *lavabo,* and he dried them upon the sleeves of his habit, for he had no napkin; then he set the second stool before him, and broke the bread upon it into five parts, in memory of the five wounds, setting two portions here and two there, and the fifth in the middle. Then he blessed the food, looking upon it a great while, and seeing with the eyes of his soul his Saviour's body stretched upon the rood. Then he began to eat, dipping each morsel into its proper wound, so that it tasted to him sweet as wine, and last of all he ate that which lay in the middle, thinking on the heart that was pierced for love of him. Then he drank water, blessed himself and gave thanks to God, and last of all poured water once more upon his hands.

Master Richard has often told me that there is no such

sweet food to be found anywhere—(save only the sacrament of the altar)—as that which is so blessed and so
eaten, and indeed I have found it so myself, when I
have had patience to do so with it.* . . .

Now God was preparing three trials for Master Richard, and the first came on the following morning very
early.

He had not slept very well; the noise from the guard-
room without was too great, and when that was quiet
there was still the foulness of the place to keep him
awake, for all the floor was strewn with rotten rags and
straw and bones, as it were a kennel. His wounds, besides, had not been tended and he was very sick when he
awoke, and for a while scarce knew where he was. I
think, perhaps, he had taken the fever then.

He heard presently steps in the way that led to his
cell, and talking, and immediately his door was un-
locked and opened. There came in a lieutenant of the
King's guard, richly dressed, and in half-armour, with
his sword at his side. He had a heavy, hairy face, and
as Master Richard sat up on his blanket he perceived
that the man was little better than an animal—gross-

* Sir John makes here a few rather trite remarks upon holy bread and
ashes and upon various methods of devotion. His words are quite irrele-
vant, therefore I omit them. He is careful, however, to warn his flock that
not every form of devotion is equally suitable for every soul.

bodied and gross-souled. I saw the fellow later, though I did not speak with him, and I judge as Master Richard judged. There were four men behind him.

Master Richard stood up immediately to salute the King's officer, and stood awaiting what should follow, but he swayed with sickness as he stood.

The officer said a word to his men, and they haled Master Richard forth, pulling him roughly, although he went willingly, as well he was able for his sickness, through the passage and into the guard-room.

There was a table set there on a step at the upper end with a chair behind it; and at the lower end was a couple of men cleaning their harness beneath a gallery that was held up by posts; the rest were out changing guard. The door into the court was wide at first, and the sweet air streamed in, refreshing Master Richard like wine after the stench that was in his nostrils, and making him think upon the country again and running water and birds, but Master-Lieutenant, when he had taken his seat, bade them close it, and to set Master Richard before him; all of which they did, and so held him.

Then he began to speak.

"Now, sir," he said roughly, "my lord King is at the point of death, and I am here to examine you. What is it that you have done to his grace?"

93

Now Master Richard knew that the King could not
die else where were the passion he was to undergo? And
if the officer could lie in this matter, why should he not
lie in other matters?

"Where is your authority," he said, "to examine me?"

"What, sir! do you question that? You shall see my
authority by and bye."

"I am willing to answer you as one man to another,"
said Master Richard softly, "but not to plead, until I
have seen your authority."

"Oh! you are willing to answer!" said the officer, smiling like an angry dog. "Very well, then. What have you
done to his grace?"

"I have done nothing," said Master Richard, "save
give the message that our Lord bade me give."

Master-Lieutenant laughed short and sharp at that,
and the two men that held Master Richard laughed with
him. (The other two men were gone to the other end of
the hall, and Master Richard could not see what they
were doing.)

"Oho!" said the officer, "that is all that you have done
to his grace! I would advise you, sir, not to play the fool
with me. We know very well what you have done; but
we would know from you how and when you did it."

Master Richard said nothing to that. He felt very light in the head, what with his wounds and the bad air, and the strangeness of the position. He knew that he was smiling, but he could not prevent it. His smiling angered the man.

"You dare smile at me, sir!" he cried. "I will teach you to smile!"—and he struck the table with his hand, so that the ink-horn danced upon it.

"I cannot help smiling," said Master Richard. "I think I am faint, sir."

One of the men shook him by the arm, and Master Richard's sense came back a little.

When he could see again clearly (for just now the face of the officer and the woodwork behind him swam like images seen in water), Master-Lieutenant had a little bottle in his hand. He bade Master Richard look upon it and asked him what it was.

"I think it to be my Quinte Essence," said Master Richard.

"You acknowledge that then!" cried the man. "And what is Quinte Essence?"

"It is distilled of blood," said Master Richard.

The officer set the bottle down again upon the table.

"Now, sir," he said, "that is enough to cast you. None

who was a Christian man would have such a thing. Say
*paternoster.**

"Paternoster . . ." began Master Richard.

Now, my children, I cannot explain what this signified,
but Master Richard could get no further than that. I
know that I myself cannot say any of the prayers of
mass when I am away from the altar, and other priests
have told me the same of themselves, but it seems to me
very strange that a man should not at any time be able
to say *paternoster*. Whether it was that Master Richard
was sick, or that the officer's face troubled him, or
whether that God Almighty desired to put him to a grievous test, I know not. But he could not say it. He repeated over and over again, *Paternoster . . . Paternoster*,
and swayed as he stood.

The officer's face grew dark and a little afraid; he
blessed himself three or four times, and breathed through
his nostrils heavily. Master Richard felt himself smiling again, and presently fell to laughing, and as he
laughed he perceived that the men who held him drew
away from him a little, and blessed themselves too.

"I cannot help it," sobbed Master Richard presently,
"to think that I cannot say *paternoster!*"

When he had recovered himself somewhat, he per-

* This seems to have been one of the tests in trials for witchcraft.

ceived that the two other men were come up behind him.

Then the officer bade him turn and look, and he did so, with the tears of that dreadful laughter still upon his cheeks.

The two men were standing there; one had a great hangman's whip of leather in his hand, and the other a rope.

"Now, sir," said the officer behind him, "here is enough authority for you and me. Shall I bid them begin, or will you tell us what it is that you have done to the King?"

Now, Master Richard had nothing to tell, as you know; he could not have saved himself in any case from the torment, but our Lord allowed him to have this trial, to see how he would bear himself. He might have cried out for mercy, or told a false tale as men so often have done, but he did neither of these things. The laughter again rose in his throat, but he drove it down, and after looking upon the men's faces and the arms of the man that held the whip, he turned once more to the officer.

"I have scourged myself too often," he said, "to fear such pain; and our Saviour bore stripes for me."

Then (for the men had released him that he might turn round) he undid the button at his throat, and threw back the kirtle, knotting the sleeves about his waist, and so stood, naked to his middle, awaiting the punishment.

He told me afterwards that never had he felt such lightness and freedom as he felt at this time. His body yearned of the pain, as it yearned for the sting and thrill of cold water on a cold day. When he was telling me, I understood better how it was that the holy martyrs were so merry in the midst of their torments.* . . .

When the officer had looked on him a moment, he bade him turn round, and so, I suppose, sat staring upon the youth's holy shoulders that were covered with the old stripes that he had given himself. At last Master Richard faced about again; and again, as he looked upon the solemn face of the man, he began to laugh. It seemed a marvellous jest, he thought, that so long a consideration should be given to so small a matter as a whipping. I am glad I was not there to hear that laughter; I think it would quite have broken my heart.

Well, my children, I cannot write what followed, but the end of it was that the post to which Master Richard's hands were tied, and the face of Master-Lieutenant standing behind it, and the wall behind him with the weapons upon it, grew white and frosted to the young man's eyes,

* Sir John relates at considerable length the Acts of St. Laurence and St. Sebastian.

and began to toss up and down, and a great roaring sounded in his ears. He thought, he told me afterwards, that he was on Calvary beneath the rood, and that the rocks were rending about him.

So he swooned clean away, and was carried back again to his prison.

Now I learned afterwards that the officer had no authority such as he pretended, but that he had sworn to his fellows that he could find out the truth by a pretence of it, thinking Master Richard to be a poor crazed fool who would cry out and confess at the touch of the whip.

But Master Richard did not cry out for mercy. And I hold that he passed this first trial bravely.

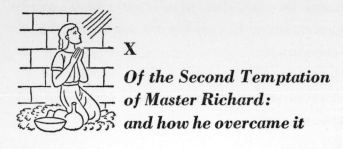

X

Of the Second Temptation of Master Richard: and how he overcame it

Exacuerunt ut gladium linguas suas: intenderunt arcum rem ama-ram: ut sagittent in occultis immaculatum.

They have whetted their tongues like a sword: they have bent their bow a bitter thing, to shoot in secret the undefiled.—*Ps. lxiii.* 4, 5.

As Master Richard had striven to serve God in the trinity of his nature, so was he to be tried in the trinity of his nature. It was first in his body that he was tempted, by pain and the fear of it; and his second trial came later in the same day—which was in his mind.

He lay abed that morning till his dinner was brought to him, knowing sometimes what passed—how a rat came out and looked on him awhile, moving its whiskers; how the patch of sunlight upon the wall darkened and passed; and how a bee came in and hummed a great while in the room; and sometimes conscious of nothing but his

100

own soul. He could make no effort, he told me, and he did not attempt it. He only lay still, committing himself to God Almighty.

He could not eat the meat, even had he wished it, but he drank a little broth and ate some bread, and then slept again.

He did not know what time it was when he awoke and found one by his bed, looking down on him, he thought, compassionately. It was growing towards evening, for it was darker, or else his eyes were heavy and confused with sickness, but he could not see very clearly the face of the man who stood by him.

The man presently kneeled down by the bed, murmuring with pity as it seemed, and Master Richard felt himself raised a little, and then laid down again, and there was something soft at the nape of his neck over the wooden pillow and against his torn shoulders. There was something, too, laid across his body and legs, as if to keep him from chill.

He said nothing for a while; he did not know what to say, but he looked steadily at the face that looked on him, and saw that it was that of a young man, not five years older than himself, shaven clean like a clerk, and the eyes of him seemed pitiful and loving.

"*Laudetur Jesus Christus!*" said Master Richard presently, as his custom was when he awoke.

"*Amen*," said the man beside the bed.

That comforted Master Richard a little—that the man should say *Amen* to his praise of Jesu Christ, so he asked him who he was and what he did there.

The young man said nothing to that, but asked him instead how he did, and his voice was so smooth and tender that Master Richard was further encouraged.

"I do far better than our Lord did," he answered. "He had none to minister to Him."

It seemed that the young man was moved at that, for he hid his face in his hands a moment.

Then he began to pity Master Richard, saying that it was a shame that he had been so evilly treated, and that Master-Lieutenant should smart for it if it ever came to his grace's ears. But he said this so strangely that Master Richard was astonished.

"And how does the King do?" he asked.

"The King is at the point of death," said the young man solemnly.

"It is no more than the point then," said Master Richard confidently, "and a point that will not pierce him, else what of the passion that he must suffer?"

The young man seemed to look on him very steadily and earnestly at that.

"Why do you look at me like that?" he asked him. "I have done nothing to his grace save give my tidings."

"Master Hermit," said the young man very gravely, "I entreat you not to speak like that."

"How should I speak then?" he asked.

The young man did not answer immediately, but he moved on his knees a little closer to the bed, and took Master Richard's hand softly between his own, and so held it, caressing it. Master Richard told me that this action moved him more than all else; he felt the tears rise to his eyes, and he gave a sob or two. It is always so with noble natures after great pain.*

Then the young man spoke very sweetly and kindly.

"Master Hermit," he said, "you must bear with me for bringing sad tidings to you. But will you hear them now or to-morrow?"

"I will hear them now," said Master Richard.

* Sir John relates here the curious history of a girl who was nearly burned as a witch, and that when she was reprieved she yielded at once to the solicitations of marriage from a man whom she had always hated, but who was the first to congratulate her on her escape. But the story sadly interrupts the drama of the main narrative, and therefore I omit it.

So the young man proceeded.

"One came back to-day from your home in the country. He was sent there yesterday night by my lord cardinal. He spoke with your parson, Sir John, and what he heard from him he has told to my lord, and I heard it."

(This was a lie, my children. No man from London had spoken with me. But you shall see what follows.)

"And what did Sir John tell him," asked Master Richard quietly. "Did he say he knew nothing of me?"

Now he asked this, thinking that perhaps this was a method of tempting him. And so it was, but worse than he thought it.

"No, poor lad," said the young man very pitifully. "Sir John knew you well enough. The messenger saw your little house, too, and the hazels about it; and the stream, and the path that you have made; and there were beasts there, he said, a stag and pig that looked lamentably out from the thicket."

Now observe the Satanic guile of this! For at the mention of all his little things, and his creatures that loved him, Master Richard could not hold back his tears, for he had thought so often upon them, and desired to see them again. So the young man stayed in his talk, and caressed his hand again, and murmured compassionately.

104

Presently Master Richard was quiet, and asked the young man to tell him what the parson had said.

"To-morrow," said the young man, making as if to rise.

"To-day," said Master Richard.

So the young man went on.

"He went to the parsonage with Sir John, and talked with him there a long while——"

"Did he see my books?" said Master Richard in his simplicity.

"Yes, poor lad; he saw your books. And then Sir John told him what he thought."

"And what was that?" said Master Richard, faint with the thought of the answer.

The young man caressed his hand again, and then pressed it as if to give him courage.

"Sir John told him that you were a good fellow; that you injured neither man nor beast; and that all spoke well of you."

Then the young man stayed again.

"Ah! tell me," cried Master Richard.

"Well, poor lad; as God sees us now, Sir John told the messenger that he thought you to be deluded; that you deemed yourself holy when you were not, and that you talked with the saints and our Lord, but that these appearances were no more than the creations of your own sick brain. He said that he humoured you; for that he feared you would be troublesome if he did not, and that all the folk of the village said the same thing to you, to please you and keep you quiet. Ah! poor child!"

The young man cried out as if in sorrow, and lifted Master Richard's hand and kissed it.

Master Richard told me that when he heard that it was as a blow in the face to him. He could not answer, nor even think clearly. It was as if a gross darkness, full of wings and eyes and mocking faces pressed upon him, and he believed that he cried out, and that he must have swooned, for when he came to himself again his face was all wet with water that the young man had thrown upon it.

It was a minute or two more before he could speak, and during that time it appeared to him that he did not think himself, but that ideas moved before his eyes, manifesting themselves. At first there was a doubt as to whether the young man had spoken the truth, and whether any messenger had been to the village at all, but the mention of the hazels, the stag and the pig, and his books, dispelled that thought.

Again it did not seem possible that the young man should have lied as to what it was that I was said to have

106

answered; if they had wished to lie, surely they would have lied more entirely, and related that I had denied all knowledge of him. But the falsehood was so subtle an one; it was so well interwoven with truth that I count it to have been impossible for Master Richard in his sickness and confusion to have disentangled the one from the other. I have heard a physician say, too, that the surest manner to perplex a man is to suggest to him that his brain is clouded; at such words he often loses all knowledge of self; he doubts his own thoughts, and even his senses.

This, then, was Master Richard's temptation—that he should doubt himself, his friends, and even our Lord who had manifested Himself so often and so kindly to the eyes of his soul.

Yet he did not yield to it, although he could not repel it. He cried upon Jesu in his heart, and then set the puzzle by.

He looked at the young man once more.

"And why do you tell me this?" he asked.

The clerk (if he were a clerk) answered him first by another Judas-caress or two, and then by Judas-words.

"Master Hermit," he said, "I am but a poor priest, but my words have some weight with two or three persons of the court; and these again have some weight with my lord cardinal. I asked leave to come and tell you this as kindly as I could, and to see what you would say. I observed you in the hall the other day, and I have a good report of your reasonableness from the monastery. I conceived, too, a great love for you when I saw you, and wish you well; and I think I can do you a great service, and get you forth from this place that you may go whither you will,—to your house by the stream or to some other place where none know you. Would it not be pleasant to you to be in the country again, and to serve God with all your might in some sweet and secret place where men are not?"

"I can serve God here as there," answered Master Richard.

"Well—let that be. But what if God Almighty wishes you to be at peace? We must not rush foolishly upon death. That is forbidden to us."

"I do not seek death," said Master Richard.

The clerk leaned over him a little, and Master Richard saw his eyes bent upon him with great tenderness.

"Master Hermit," he said, "I entreat you not to be your own enemy. You see that those that know you best love you, but they do not think you to be what you think you are——"

"I am nothing but God's man, and a sinner," said the lad.

"Well, they think your visions and the rest to be but delusions. And if they be delusions, why should not other matters be delusions too?"

"What matters?" asked Master Richard.

"Such matters as the tidings that you brought to the King."

"And what is it you would have me to do?" asked Master Richard again after a silence.

"It is only a little thing, poor lad—such a little thing! and then you will be able to go whither you will."

"And what is that little thing?"

"It is to tell me that you think them delusions too."

"But I do not think them so," said Master Richard.

"Think as you will then, Master Hermit; but, you know, when folks are sick we may tell them anything without sin. And the King is sick to death. I do not believe that you have bewitched him: you have too good a face and air for that—and for the matter of the *paternoster* I do not value it at a straw. The King is sick with agony at what he thinks will come upon him after your words. He will not listen to my lord cardinal: he sits silent and terrified, and has taken no food to-day. But if you will but tell him, Master Hermit, that you were mistaken in your tidings—that it was but a fancy, and that you know better now—all will be well with him and with you, and with us all who love you both."

So the clerk spoke, tempting him, and leaned back again on his heels; and Master Richard lay a great while silent.

Now, I do not know who was this young man, whether he were a clerk or whether he were not a devil in form of a man. I could hear nothing of him at Court when I went there. It may be that he was one of those idle fellows that had come to Master Richard from time to time to ask him to make them hermits with him, else how did he know the matters of the stag and the pig and the stream and the rest? But it does not greatly matter whether his soul were a devil's or a man's, for in any case his words were Satan's. If I had not heard what came after I should have believed this temptation to be the most subtle ever devised in hell and permitted from heaven. He spoke so tenderly and so sweetly; he commanded his features so perfectly; he seemed to speak with such love and reasonableness.

Yet I would have you know that Master Richard did not yield by a hair's breadth in thought. He examined the temptation carefully, setting aside altogether the question as to whether I had spoken as this young man had said that I had. Whether I had spoken so or not made no difference. It was this that he was bidden to do, to say that he had erred in his tidings, to confess that they were not from God; to be a faithless messenger to our Lord.

He examined this, then, looking carefully at all parts of the temptation.*. . .

At the end Master Richard opened his eyes and looked steadily upon the young man's face.

"Take this answer," he said, "to those that sent you. I will neither hear nor consider such words any more. If I yield in this matter, and say one word to the King or to any other, by which any may understand that my message was a delusion, or that I spoke of myself and not from our Lord, then I pray that our Lord may blot my name out of the Book of Life."

So Master Richard answered and closed his eyes to commune with God. And the young man went away sighing but speaking no word.

* Sir John appends at this point two or three paragraphs, distinguishing between the observing of a temptation of thought and the yielding to it. He instances Christ's temptation in the Garden of Gethsemane.

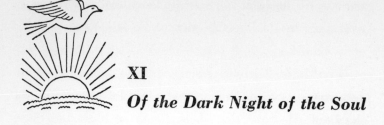

XI

Of the Dark Night of the Soul

De profundis clamavi ad te, Domine: Domine exaudi vocem meam.

Out of the depths I have cried to Thee, O Lord: Lord, hear my voice.
—*Ps. cxxix.* 1, 2.

THE third temptation was so fierce and subtle, that I doubt whether I wholly understood it when Master Richard tried to tell it to me. He did not tell me all, and he could answer but few questions, and I fear that I am not able to tell even all that I heard from him. It was built up like a house, he said, stone by stone, till it fenced him in, but he did not know what was all its nature till he saw my lord cardinal.

A soul such as was Master Richard's must have temptations that seem as nothing to coarser brings such as myself: as a bird that lives in the air has dangers that a crawling beast cannot have. There are perils in the height that are not perils on the earth. A bird may strike a tree or a tower; his wings may fail him; he may fly too near

112

the sun till he faint in its heat; he cannot rest; if he is overtaken by darkness he cannot lie still.*

Now Master Richard described the state into which he fell under a curious name that I cannot altogether understand. He said that there be three *nights* through which the contemplative soul must pass or ever it come to the dawn. The first two he had gone through during his life in the country; the first is a kind of long-continued dryness, when spiritual things have no savour; the second is all affection of the mind, when not even meditation† appears possible; the mind is like a restless fly that is at once weary and active. This second is not often attained to by ordinary souls, though all men who serve God have a shadow of it. It is a very terrible state. Master Richard told me that before he suffered it he had not conceived that such conflict was possible to man. It was during this time that the fiend came to him in form of a woman. The imagination that cannot fix itself upon the things of God is wide-awake to all other impressions of sense.‡ . . .

* Sir John enumerates at some length other such dangers to bird life.

† This is an exercise distinct from contemplation apparently. I include this passage, in spite of its technicalities, for obvious reasons.

‡ I do not think that Sir John understands what he is writing about, though he does his best to appear as if he did. I have omitted a couple of incoherent paragraphs.

Now, these two first *nights* I think I understand, for he told me that what he suffered during his whipping in the hall and the strife of his mind with the clerk were each a kind of symbol of them. But the third, which he called the *Night of the Soul* I do not understand at all.* This only can I say of the state itself—that Master Richard said that it was in a manner what our Lord suffered upon the rood when he cried to His Father, *Eloi, Eloi, etc.*

But I can tell you something of the signs of that affliction, as they shewed themselves to Master Richard. Of the interior state of his soul I cannot even think without terror and confusion. Compared with the darkness of it, the other *nights*, he said, are but as clouds across the sun on a summer's day compared with a moonless midnight in winter. He had suffered a shadow of it before, when he was entering the contemplative state, or the perfect Way of Union. Now it fell upon him. Before I tell you how it came, I must tell you that this *night*, as he explained it, takes its occasion from some particular thought, and the thought from which it sprang you shall hear presently.

* It is remarkable that this phrase frequently occurs in the writings of St. John of the Cross, though he treats it differently. Until I came across it in this MS. I had always thought that the Spanish mystic was the first to use it.

When the clerk had left him, sighing, as I said, as if with a kindly weariness (to encourage the other to call for him, I suppose), Master Richard committed himself again to God and lay still.

A fellow came in soon with his supper (for it was now growing dark), set it by him and went out. Master Richard took a little food, and after a while, as his custom was after repeating the name of Jesu, began to think on God, on the Blessed and Holy Trinity, and on His attributes, numbering them one by one and giving thanks for each, and marking the colour and place of each in the glory of the throne. He was too weary to say vespers or compline, and presently he fell asleep, but whether it was common sleep or not I do not know.

In his sleep it seemed to him that he was walking along a path beneath trees, as he had walked on his way to London; but it was twilight, and he could not see clearly. There was none with him, and he was afraid, and did not know what he feared. He was afraid of what lay behind, and on all sides, and he was yet more afraid of what lay before him, but he knew that he could not stay nor turn. He went swiftly, he thought, and with no sound, towards some appointed place, and the twilight darkened as he went; when he looked up there was no star nor moon to be seen, and what had been branches when he set out seemed now to be a roof, so thick they were. There was no bray of stag, nor rustle of breeze, nor cry of night-bird. He tried to pray, but he could remember no prayer, and not even the healthful name of *Jesu* came to his mind. He could do nought but look outwards with his straining eyes, and inwards at his soul; and the one was now as dark as the other. He thought of me then, my children, and longed to have me there, but he knew that I was asleep in my bed and far away. He thought of his mother whom he had loved so much, but he knew that she was gone to God and had left him alone. And still, through all, his feet bore him on swiftly without sound or fatigue, though the terror and the darkness were now black as ink. He felt his hair rising upon his head, and his skin prickle, and the warmth was altogether gone from his heart, but he could not stay.

And at the last his feet ceased to move, and he stood still, knowing that he was come to the place.

Now, I do not understand what he said to me of that place. He told me that he could see nothing; it was as if his eyes were put out, yet he knew what it was like.

It was a little round place in the forest, with trees standing about it, and it was trampled hard with the footsteps of those who had come there before him. But that was no comfort to him now; for he did not know how these persons had fared, nor where were their souls.

So he stood in the black darkness, knowing that he could not turn, with the horror on him so heavy that he sweated as he told me of it, and with the knowledge that something was approaching under the trees without sound of step or breathing—he did not know whether it was man or beast or fiend, he only knew that it was approaching. Yet he could not pray or cry out.

Then he was aware that it had entered the little space where he stood, and was even now within a hand's grasp. Yet he could not lift his hands to ward it off, or to pray to God, or to bless himself.

Then he perceived that the thing—*negotium perambulans in tenebris**—was formless, without hands to strike or mouth to bite him with, and that it was all about him now, closing upon him. If there had been aught to touch his body, wet lips to kiss his face, or fiery eyes to look into his own, he would not have feared it with a thousandth part of the fear that he had. It was that there was no shape or face, and that it sought not his body but his soul. And when he understood that he gave a loud cry and awoke, and knew, as in a mystery, that it was no

* "The Business that walketh about in the dark" (Ps. xc. 6).

117

dream, but that he was indeed come to the place that he had seen, and that the *negotium* was at his soul's heart* . . .

I find it impossible, my children, to make you understand in what state he was; he could not make even me understand. I can only set down a little of what he said.

First, he knew that he had lost God. It was not that there was no God, but that he had lost Him of his own fault and sin. He was aware that in all other places there was God and that the blessed reigned with Him, but not in the place where he was, nor in his heart. In all men that ever I have met there was a certain presence of God. As the apostle told the men of Athens, *Ipsius enim et genus suum;*† and, again, *Non longe est ab unoquoque nostrum;*‡ and again, *In ipso vivimus, et movemur, et sumus.*§ I have not seen a man who had not this knowledge, though maybe some, such as Turks and pagans, may call it by another name. But until death, I think, all men, whatever their sins or ignorance, live and move in God's Majesty. Hell, Master Richard told me, is nothing less than the withdrawal of that presence, with other tor-

* There is either an omission here in the translation of Sir John's original MS., or else the transcriber has dashed his pen down in horror, or sought to produce an impression of it.
† "For we are also His offspring" (Acts xvii. 28).
‡ "He is not far from every one of us" (Acts xvii. 27).
§ "In Him we live, and we move, and we are" (Acts xvii. 28).

118

ments superadded, but this is chief. Master Richard told me that that black fire of hell rages wherever God is not; and that the worm gnaws in all hearts that have lost Him, and know it to be by their own fault—*maxima culpa.**

There be a few men in this world—the Son of God derelict is their prince—who are called to this supreme torment while they yet live—if indeed that man may be said to live who is without God—and of this company Master Richard was now made one.

It was with him now as he had dreamed. Where God is not, there can be no communion with man, for the only reason by which one perceives another's soul, or understands that it is the soul of a man and has a likeness to his own, is that both are, in some measure, in God. If we were more holy and wise we should understand for ourselves that this is so, and see, too, why it is so, for He is eyes to the blind and ears to the deaf.†

For Master Richard, then, there was no other person in the world. There was that that fenced him from all living. Our Saviour Christ upon the rood spoke to His Blessed Mother before His dereliction, but not again afterwards. There was no more that He might say to her, or to His cousin, John.

* The very great fault.
† I do not understand this at all. I wonder whether Sir John did, as he wrote it; I am quite sure that his flock did not.

This, then, was the state in which Master Richard lay
—that *specialissimus* of God Almighty, to whom the Divine Love and Majesty was as breath to his nostrils, meat
to his mouth, and water to his body. I can say no more
on that point.

As to the fault by which it seemed that he had come
to that state it was the most terrible of all sins, which is
Presumption. Holy Church sets before us Humility as the
chief of virtues, to shew us that Presumption is the chief
of vices. A man may be an adulterer or a murderer or a
sacrilegious person, and yet by Humility may find
mercy. But a man may be chaste and stainless in all his
works, and a worshipper of God, but without Humility
he cannot come to glory.* . . .

Now the matter in which it seemed to Master Richard
that he had sinned the sin of Presumption was the old
matter of the tidings he had borne to the King. It was not
that the tidings were false, for he knew them for true;
but yet that he had been presumptuous in bearing them.
It was as though a stander-by had overheard tidings
given by a king to his servant, and had presumed to bear
them himself, as it were Achimaas the son of Sadoc.†

---

* Sir John proceeds in this strain for several pages, illustrating his
point by the cases of Lucifer, Nabuchodonosor, Judas Iscariot, King Herod,
and others.

† I suppose that this obscure reference is to 2 Kings xviii. 19.

And more than that, that he had presumed in thinking that he could be such a man as our Lord would call to such an office. He had set himself, it appeared, far above his fellows in even listening to our Saviour's voice; he should rather have cried with saint Peter, *Exi a me quia homo peccator sum Domine.**

It was this sin that had driven him from God's Presence. Our Lord had bestowed on him wonderful gifts of grace. He had visited him as He visits few others and had led him in the Way of Union, and he had followed, triumphing in this, giving God the glory in words only, until he had fallen as it seemed from the height of presumption to the depth of despair, and lay here now, excluded from the Majesty that he desired.

Now, here is a very wonderful thing, and I know not if I can make it clear.

You understand, my children, a little of what I heard from Master Richard's lips—of what it was that he suffered. But although all this was upon him, he perceived afterwards, though not at the time, that there was something in him that had not yielded to the agony. His body was broken, and his mind amazed, and his soul obscured in this *Night*, yet there was one power more, that we name

* "Depart from me, for I am a sinful man, O Lord" (Luke v. 8).

121

the Will (and that is the very essence of man, by which he shall be judged), that had not yet sunk or cried out that it was so as the fiend suggested.

There was within him, he perceived afterwards, a conflict without movement. It was as when two men wrestle, their limbs are locked, they are motionless, they appear to be at rest, but in truth they are striving with might and main.

So he remained all that night in this agony, not knowing that he did aught but suffer; he saw the light on the wall, and heard the cocks crow—at least he remembered these things afterwards. But his release did not come until the morning; and of that release, and its event, and how it came about, I will now tell you.

XII

How Sir John went again to the cell: and of what he saw there

---

Ecce audivimus eam in Ephrata: invenimus eam in campis silvae.

Behold we have heard of it in Euphrata: we have found it in the fields of the wood.—*Ps. cxxxi.* 6.

It is strange to think that other men went about their business in the palace, and knew nothing of what was passing. It is more strange that that morning I said mass in the country and did not faint for fear or sorrow. But it is always so, by God's loving-kindness, for no man could bear to live if he knew all that was happening in the world at one time.* . . .

There was a little heaviness upon me that morning, but I think no more than there had been every day since Master Richard had left us. It was not until noon that a strange event happened to me. This day was Wednesday after Corpus Christi, the sixth day since he was gone.

* Sir John adds some trite reflections of an obvious character.

123

There was only one man that knew aught of what was passing in the interior world, and that was the ankret in the cell against the abbey, but of that you shall hear in the proper place.

Of what fell on that day I heard from an old priest whom I saw afterwards, and who was in the palace at that time. He was chaplain to my lord cardinal and his name was . . . .

He told me that very early in the morning my lord sent for him and told him that he would hold an examination of Master Richard that day after dinner, to see if he should be put on his trial for bewitching the King. There were none who doubted that he had bewitched the King, for his grace had sat in a stupor for two days, ever since he had heard the tidings from the holy youth. He heard his masses each morning with a fallen countenance, and took a little food in private, and slept in his clothes sitting in his chair; and spoke to none, and, it seemed, heard none. Though he had been always of a serious and quiet mind, loving to pray and to hear preaching more than to talk, yet this was the first of those strange visitations of God that fell upon him so frequently in his later years. Those then (and especially my lord cardinal) who now saw him in such a state, did not doubt that there was sorcery in the matter, and that

Master Richard was the sorcerer; for the tale of the Quinte Essence—of which at that time men knew nothing—and how that he could not say *paternoster* when it was put to him;—all this was run about the court like fire.

But the tale of the clerk who went to him and sought to shake him, I heard nothing of, save from Master Richard's own lips. None knew of what had happened, and some afterwards thought that it was the fiend who went to Master Richard, but some others that it was indeed one of the clerks of the court who had perhaps stolen the keys, and gone in to get credit to himself by persuading Master Richard to confess that all was a delusion. For myself, I do not know what to think.* . . .

Now, old Master . . . . said mass before my lord cardinal at seven o'clock, and then went to his own chamber, but he was immediately sent for again to my lord, who appeared to be in a great agitation. My lord told him that one had come from the ankret to bid him let Master Richard go, for that it was not the young man who was afflicting the King, but God Almighty.

"But he shall not play Pilate's wife with me," said my

* I suspect that Sir John was inclined to think it was the devil, for at this point he discusses at some length various cases in which Satan so acted. He seems to imply that it was a peculiar and cynical pleasure to the Lord of Evil to disguise himself as an ecclesiastic.

lord in a great fury, "I shall go through with this matter. See that you be with me, Master Priest, at noon, and we will see justice done. I doubt not that the young man must go for his trial."

He told the clerk, too, that Master Blytchett was greatly concerned about his grace, and that the court would be in an uproar if somewhat were not done at once. He had sat three hours last night with . . . . and . . . . and . . . . and . . . .*, and they had all declared the same thing. But he said nothing of the whipping of Master Richard, and I truly believe that he knew nothing of it.

So the hour for the questioning was fixed at noon, and the place to be in my lord cardinal's privy parlour.

Now that morning, as I told you, I was no more than usually heavy. I remembered Master Richard's name before God upon the altar, and at ten o'clock I went to dinner in the parsonage. It was a very bright hot day, and I had the windows wide, and listened to the bees that were very busy in the garden. I remember that I wondered whether they knew aught of my dear lad, for I hold that they are very near to God, more so than perhaps any of His senseless creatures, and that is why

---

* It would be interesting to know who were these persons.

Richard Raynal

Holy Church on Easter Eve says such wonderful things about them, and the work that they do.*

For they fashion first wax and then honey. It is the wax that in the church gives light and honour to God, and it is to the honeycomb that God's Word is compared by David.† . . .

It is not strange then that I thought about the bees, and the knowledge that they have.

After I had done dinner, I slept a little as my custom is, and the last sound that I heard, and the first upon awaking, was the drone of the bees. When I awakened I thought that I would walk down to Master Richard's house and see how all fared. So I took my staff and set out.

It was very cool and dark in the wood, through which I had come up six days before walking in the summer night with the young man, and all was very quiet. I could hear only the hum of the flies, and, as I drew nearer, the running of the water over the stones of the road, where it crosses it beside the little bridge.

Then I came out beside the gate into the meadow, and my eyes were dazzled by the hot light of the sun after the darkness of the wood.

* This refers to the *Exultet* sung by the deacon in the Roman rite on Holy Saturday.
† Sir John continues in this strain for a page or two.

I stood by the gate a good while, leaning my arms upon it (for I felt very heavy and weary), and looking across the meadow yellow with flowers to the green hazels beyond, and between me and the wood the air shook as if in terror or joy, I knew not which. I could see, too, the open door of the hut, and its domed roof of straw, and the wicket leaning against the wall as he had left it, and on either side the may-trees lifted their bright heads.

My children, I am not ashamed to tell you that I could not see all this very clearly, for my eyes were dim at the thought that the master of it was not here, and that I knew not where he was nor how he fared. I prayed saint Giles with all my might that I might see him here again, and walk with him as I had walked so often. And then at the end, a little after I had heard the *Angelus* ring from over the wood, and had saluted our Lady and entreated her for Master Richard, I thought that I would go up and see the hut.

As I went I perceived that here, too, the bees were busy in the noon of the day, going to and fro intently, but I was to see yet more of them, for I heard a great droning about me. At first I could not perceive whence it came, but presently I saw a great ball of them gathering on the doorway of the hut, as their custom is in summer-time. I was astonished at that, I do not know why, but it seemed to me that bees were all about me, *semitam meam et funiculum meum investigantes; omnes vias meas praevidentes.** Well, I looked on them awhile, but they seemed as if they would do me no harm, yet I did not wish to go into the house while they hung there, so I was content with looking in from where I stood. I could not see very much, my eyes were too heavy with the sunshine that beat on my head, and it was, perhaps, God's purpose that I should not go in to see what I was not worthy to see.

I had, too, something of fear in my heart; it was like the fear that I had had when I looked on Master Richard six days before as he prayed. So I stood a little distance from the door and observed it and the bees. Of the inside of the hut I could see no more than the beaten mud floor for a little space within, and through the veil of bees that swung this way and that working their mysteries, the green light of the window looking upon the hazel wood, above which was the image of the Mother of God.

Then on a sudden my fear came on me strongly, and I cried out what I think was Master Richard's name, for I thought that he was near me, but there was no answer,

* "Searching out my path and my line; foreseeing all my ways" (from Ps. cxxxix. 3, 4).

and after I had looked a little more, I turned back by the way I had come.

Now, here, my children, happened a marvellous thing.

When I reached the gate and had gone through it, I turned round again towards the hut, ashamed of the terror that had lain on me as I walked down, for I had walked like one in a nightmare, not daring to turn my head.

And as I turned, for one instant I saw Master Richard himself, in his brown kirtle and white sleeves standing at the door of his hut, with his arms out as if to stretch himself, or else as our Saviour stretched them on the rood. I could not observe his face, for in an instant he was gone, before I had time to see him clearly, but I am sure that his face was merry, for it was at this hour that he found his release before my lord cardinal, and cried out, as you shall hear in the proper place.

I stood there a long while, stretching out my own hands and crying on him by name, but there was no more to be seen but the hut and its open door, and the may-trees on either side, and the wood behind, and the yellow-flowered meadow before me, and no sound but the drone of the bees and the running of the water. And I dared not go up again, or set foot in the meadow.

130

Richard Raynal

So I went home again, and told no man, for I thought that the vision was for myself alone, and as night fell the messenger came to bid me come to town, and to deliver to me the letter from the old priest of whom I have spoken.

XIII

How one came to Master Priest: how Master Priest came to the King's Bed-chamber: and of what he heard of the name of Jesus

---

Dum anxiaretur cor meum: in petra exaltasti me.

When my heart was in anguish: Thou hast exalted me on a rock.
—*Ps. lx.* 3.

THIS was the letter that I read in my parlour that night, as the man in his livery stood beside me, dusty with riding. I have it still (it is in the mass-book that stands beside my desk; you can find it there after I am gone to give my account).

"REVEREND AND RIGHT WORSHIPFUL SIR JOHN CHALD-
        FIELD,—

"There is a young man here named Master Richard Raynal, who tells us that you are his friend. He desires to see you before his death, for he has been set upon and will not live many days. His grace has ordered that you

132

shall be brought with speed, for he loves this young man and counts him a servant of God. He is with Master Raynal as I write. I fear this may be heavy news for you, Sir John, so I will write no more, but I recommend myself to you, and pray that you may be comforted and speeded here by the grace of God, which ever have you in His keeping.

"Written at Westminster, the Wednesday after Corpus Xti.

"Yours,

".   .   .   .   ."

I asked the fellow who brought the letter whether he could tell me any more, but all that he could say was that he was in the court outside my lord cardinal's privy stairs—where the people were assembled to see Master Richard come out, and that he had seen a confusion, and blows struck, and the glaivemen run in to help him. Then he had seen no more, but he thought Master Richard had been taken back again to the palace, and heard that he had been sore wounded and beaten, and was not like to live.

I will not tell you, my children, of my ride to London that night, save that I do not think I ceased praying from the instant that I set out to the instant when I came up as the dawn began behind Lambeth House, and we went over in the ferry. I cried in my heart with David, *Fili mi, Fili mi; quis mihi tribuat ut ego moriar pro te, fili mi, fili mi?** And I prayed two things—that God might forgive me for having allowed the lad to go, and that I might find him alive. More than that I dared not pray, and I know not even now if I should have prayed the first.

It was a wonderful dawn that I saw as I crossed over, with a mist coming up from the water as a promise of great heat, and above it the high roofs and towers like the lovely city of God, and over all the sky was of a golden colour with lines of pearl across it. It comforted me a little that I should come to Master Richard so.

Even at that hour there were many awake. There was one great fellow by the ferry, that was looking across towards the palace; and I think it must have been he who had taken Master Richard over for love of saint Giles and saint Denis, but I did not know that part of the tale at that time, and I never saw him again.

In the court and passages, too, that we went along there were persons going to and fro. One told me afterwards that never had he seen such a movement at that

---

* "My son, my son! Who would grant that I might die for thee, my son, my son?"—2 Kings xviii. 33.

hour since the night that the King's mother died. They were all waiting for tidings of the lad, and they eyed me very narrowly, and I heard my name run before me as I went.

At the last we came to a great door, and we were let through, and I was in the King's bed-chamber.

It was a quiet room, and I will describe it to you now, although I saw little of it at that time.

In the centre, with its head against the wall, stood a tall bed, with a canopy over it, and four posts of twisted wood, carved very cunningly with little shields that bore the instruments of our Saviour's passion. On the tapestry beneath the canopy, above the pillow, were the arms of the King, wrought in blue and red and gold. The hangings on the walls were all of a dark blue, wrought with devices of all kinds, and they were hanged from a ledge of wood beneath the ceiling such as I have never seen before or since. The ceiling was of painted wood, divided into deep squares, and in the centre of each was a coat. The floor was all over rushes, the cleanest and the most fragrant that I have ever smelled. I think that there must have been herbs and bay leaves mixed with them.

I saw all this afterwards, for when I came in the curtains were all drawn against the windows, save against one that let in the cool air from the river and a little pale light of morning, and two candles burned on a table beside the bed. The room was very dark, but I could see that a dozen persons stood against the walls, and one by every door.

But I had no eyes for them, and went quickly across the rushes, and as I came round the foot of the bed, I heard my name whispered again, and the King stood up from where he had been kneeling.

I have already described to you his appearance at that time, so I will say no more here than that he was in all his clothes which were a little disordered, and that his head was bare. He had been weeping, too, for his eyes were red and swollen, and his lips shook as he put out his hand. But he could not speak.

I kneeled down and kissed his hand quickly and stood up immediately. Master Richard who was lying on his left side, turned away from me, so that I could not see his face, but I knew he was not yet dead, else he would have been laid upon his back, but he was as still as death. His head was all in a bandage, except on this side where his long hair hung across his cheek, and his bare arm lay across the rich coverlet, brown to the elbow with his digging, and white as milk at the shoulder.

When I saw that I kneeled down too, and hid my face

in my hands, and although I felt the King lay his fingers
on my shoulder I could not look up. But it was not all
for sorrow that I wept; I was thanking God Almighty
who permitted me to see Master Richard alive once
more.

I do not know how long it was before I looked up, but
all the folks were gone from the room save the King, and
Master Blytchett, the physician, who sat on the other
side of the bed.

I went round presently to the other side, the King going with me, and there I saw Master Richard's face. I cannot tell you all that I saw in it, for there are no words
that can tell of its peace; his eyes were closed below the
little healed scar that he had taken in the monastery, and
his lips were open and smiling; they moved two or three
times as I looked, as if he were talking with some man,
and then they ceased and smiled again. But all was very
little, as if the soul were far down in some secret chamber
with company that it loved.

I asked presently if he had received his Maker, and
the King told me Yes, and shrift too, and anointing—all
the night before when he had come to himself for a while
and called for a priest. He had spoken my name, too, at
that time and they had told him that one was gone to
bring me and at that he seemed content.

Master Blytchett told me soon that I could be gone for a while, to take some meat, and that he would send for me if Master Richard awoke. But I said No to that; until the King bade me go, saying that he, too, would remain, and pledging his word that I should be called.

So I went away into a parlour, and washed myself, and took some food, and after a while the old clerk that had written the letter to me, came in and saluted me.

I was desirous to know how all had come about, so we sat there a great while in the window seat, with the door a little open into the bed-chamber, and he told me the tale. I did not speak one word till he had done.

This was how it came about.

Master Richard was sent for from his cell to the parlour of my lord cardinal, but my lord was not ready for him, and he had to stand a great while in the court to wait his pleasure. The rumour ran about as to who it was, and a great number of persons assembled from all parts, some from the palace, and some from the streets. These had so cried out against the young man, that the bill-men were sent for from the guard-room to keep him from their violence. This priest had looked out from a window at the noise, and seeing the crowd, had entreated my lord to have the prisoner in without any more delay. So he was brought in, and one was left to keep the little door that led to the privy stairs up which he came.

It was then that this priest had seen him face to face, and I will try to write down his words as he told them me.

"I came into the parlour," he said, "through the door behind my lord's chair, as Master Raynal was brought in by the other door.

"I have never seen such a sight, Sir John, as I saw then. He was in his white kirtle only, with the five wounds upon his breast, and he had on his sandals. But his face was as that of a dead man: his eyelids were sunk upon his cheek, and his lips hung open so that I could see his bare teeth.

"There were two men who led him by the arms, and he would have fallen but for their assistance, and I immediately whispered to my lord to let him sit down. But my lord was busy and anxious at that time, for he had but just come from the King, who was no better and would take no meat nor speak at all. So he paid no heed to me, and presently began to ask questions of Master Raynal, urging him to confess what it was that he had done, and threatening him with this and that if he would not speak.

"But Master Raynal did not speak or lift his eyes; it seemed as if he did not hear one word.

"My lord told him presently that if temporal pains did not move him, perhaps, it was that he desired spiritual—for my lord was very angry, and scarce knew what he was saying. But Master Richard made no answer. I will tell you, Sir John, plainly, that I thought he was but a fool to anger my lord so by his silence, for it could not be that he did not hear: my lord bawled loud enough to awaken the dead, and I saw the folk behind, some laughing and some grave.

"It would be full half an hour after noon before my lord had done his questions, and lay back in his chair wrathful at getting no answer, though the men that held Master Raynal shook him from side to side.

"Then it was that the end came.

"I was observing Master Raynal very closely, wondering whether he were mad or deaf, and on a sudden he lifted his eyes, and his lips closed. He appeared to be looking at my lord, but it was another that he saw.

"I cannot describe to you, Sir John, what that change was that came to him, save by saying that I think Lazarus must have looked like that, as he heard our Saviour Christ's voice calling to him as he lay in the tomb. It was no longer the face of a dead man, but of a living

140

one, and as that change came, I perceived that my lord
cardinal had raised himself in his chair, and was staring, I suppose at the young man too. But I could not take
my eyes off Master Raynal's face.

"Then on a sudden Master Raynal smiled and drew a
great breath and cried out. It was but one word; it was
the holy Name of JESUS.

"I perceived immediately that my lord cardinal had
stood up at that cry, but then he sat down again, and he
made a motion with his hand, and the men that held
Master Raynal wheeled him about, and they went
through the crowd towards the door.

"My lord cardinal turned to me, and I have never
seen him so moved, but still he could not speak, and
while we looked upon one another there was a great uproar everywhere—in the court and in the palace.

"I stood there, not knowing what to do, and my lord
pushed past to the window. He, too, cried out as he
looked down, and then ran from the room, and as I was
following there broke in one by the door behind the
chair.

" 'Where is my lord cardinal?' he cried: 'The King
has sent for him.'

"Well, the end of the matter was that they brought
Master Raynal back again, wounded and battered near

to death. The crowd that had been attendant for him had set on him as he came out—they should have sent more bill-men before to keep the road, and the King met him in the way (for he had come to his senses again), and turned as white as ashes once more, crying out that his own craven heart had slain one more* servant of God, but I know not what he meant by that. Master Raynal was taken to the King's bed-chamber, and my lord came after. And the King has been with him, praying and moaning ever since."

Then I put one question to the priest.

"My lord cardinal?" I said.

"No man but the King has seen my lord cardinal since yesterday."

We sat a while longer in silence, and then Master Blytchett came in to see me.

* If this king was Henry VI. the reference may be to Joan of Arc. But Henry was only a child at the time of her death. At best this can be only conjecture.

142

XIV

Of Sir John's Meditations in Westminster Palace

Existimabam ut cognoscerem hoc: labor est ante me.

I studied that I might know this thing: it is a labour in my sight.
—*Ps. lxxii.* 16.

MASTER BLYTCHETT told me that Master Richard was still asleep. He had blooded him last night, and reduced the fever, but God only could save his life. For himself, he thought that the young man would die before night, and he did not know whether he would speak again.

I was drawn towards Master Blytchett; he seemed a sour fellow with sweetness beneath; and I love such souls as that. I loved him more than I did the King either at that time or afterward. The King appeared to me at that time a foolish fellow—God forgive me!—for I had not then heard what Master Richard had to say to him; nor that such opinion was to be all part of his passion.

143

I thanked Master Blytchett for what he had done for my lad; but he burst out upon me.

"I was all against him," he said, "at the beginning. I thought him a crack-brained fool, and a meddler. But now——" And he would say no more.

It seemed that many were like that at the Court. They were near all against him at first; but when they knew that he was wounded to death; and had heard what the King had said of him; and seen my lord cardinal's rosy face running with tears of pity and anger as he tore the lad out of their hands; and gossiped a little with the porter of the monastery; and listened to the holy ankret roaring out in his cell against Hierusalem that slew the prophets;—and, most of all, remembered, or told one another of Master Richard's face as he came out from the privy staircase before he was struck down—like the Melitenses—*convertentes se dicebant eum esse deum.**

I talked with many that morning (for I could do nothing for my lad), who came in to see one who knew him so well, and had been his friend in the country.

And after dinner my lord cardinal came in to see me, and I was brought back to the parlour.

His ruddy face was all blotched and lined with sor-

* "Changing their minds, they said he was a god" (Acts xxviii. 6).

row or age, and for a while he could say nothing. He went up and down with his sanguine robes flying behind him, and stayed to look out of the window at the boats that went by until I thought that he had forgotten me. And at the last he spoke.

"I do not know what to say to you, Sir John, or what to say to God Almighty on this matter. It appears to me that we have all been blind and deaf adders, and with the venom of adders, too, beneath our tongues—except one or two rude fellows, and my lord King who knew him for a prophet, and the ankret, who tells us we shall all be damned for what we have done, and yourself. There be so many of these wild asses that bray and kick, that when he came we did not distinguish him to be the colt on which our Lord came to town—and now, as it was then, *Dominus eum necessarium habet.**

"But I know what I wish to be said to him, though I dare not say it myself, or set eyes on him—and that is that I pray him to forgive us, and to speak our names before the Lord God when he comes before His Majesty."

"I will tell him that, my lord," I said softly, for I did not doubt that Master Richard would speak before he died.

After a while longer my lord cardinal asked how he

* "The Lord hath need of him" (Luke xix. 34).

145

did, and I told him that he had lain very quiet all day without speaking or moving, and then, for I knew what my lord wanted, I bade him in Jesu's name to come in and look on him. For a while he would not, and then he came, and knelt down beside the King.

Master Richard was lying now upon his back, with his hands hidden and clasped upon his breast, and his lips were moving a little without sound. I think that he had never had so long and so heavenly a colloquy as he was enjoying then. I do not know whether it were the cardinal's presence that disturbed him, or whether in that secret place where his soul was retired he heard what had been said by us, but he spoke aloud for the first time that day, and this is what he said:—

"Et dimitte nobis debita nostra; sicut et nos dimittimus debitoribus nostris."*

I saw my lord's face go down upon his hands, and the King's face rise and look at him. And presently my lord went out.

I cannot tell you, my children, how that day passed, for it was like no day that I have ever spent. It appeared to me that there was no time, but that all stood still. Without, the palace was as still as death on the one side—for

---

* "And forgive us our trespasses, as we forgive them that trespass against us."

146

the King had ordered it so—and on the other there was the noise from the river, little and clear and distinct, of the water washing in the sedges and against the stones, and the cries of the boatmen on the further shore, and the rattle of their oars as they took men across.

Once, as I stood by the window saying my office, a boat went by with folk talking in it, and I heard enough of what they said to know that they were speaking of Master Richard, and I heard one telling the tale to another, and saw him point to the windows of the palace. But when they saw me look out they gave over talking.

A little after the evening bell Master Blytchett took the King out to his supper, and I was left alone with Master Richard, but I knew that there were servants in the passage whom I might call if I needed them.

So I sat down by the pillow and looked at him a great while.

I will tell you, my children, something of what I thought at this time, for it is at such times when the eyes are washed clean by tears that the soul looks out upon truth and sees it as it is.* . . .

---

* I have omitted a great number of Sir John's reflections. Many of them are too trite even for this work, and others are so much confused that it is useless to transcribe them. Sir John seems to have been dearly fond of sermonising. Even these that I have retained and set within brackets can be omitted in reading by those who prefer to supply their own comment.

[I thought of the *ironia* that marks our Lord's dealings. Master Richard had come to bring tidings of another's passion, and he found his own in the bringing of it. It was as when children play at the hanging of a murderer or a thief, and one is set to play the part of prisoner and another to hang him, and then at the end when all is prepared they turn upon the hangman and bid him prepare himself for whipping and death instead of the other, or maybe both are to be hanged. But our Lord is not cruel, like such children, but kind, and I think that He acts so to shew us that life is nothing but a play and a pretence, and that His will must be done, however much we rebel at it. He teaches us, too, that the blows we receive and even death itself are only seeming, though they hurt us at the time, but that we must play in a gallant and merry spirit, and be tender, too, and forgive one another easily, and that He will set all right and allot to each his reward at the end of the playing. And, since it is but a play, we are none of us kings or cardinals or poor men in reality; we are all of us mere children of our Father, and upon one is set a crown for a jest, and another is robed in sanguine, and another in a brown kirtle or a white; and at the end the trinkets are all put back again in the press, ready for another day and other children, and we all go to bed as God made us.

But you must not think, my children, that our life is a little thing because of this; I only mean that one thing is as little and as great as another, and that maids maying in the country are as much about God's business as kings and cardinals who strive in palaces, and who give to this man a collar of Saint Spirit, and to that man a collar of hemp. It was for this reason, maybe, that our Lord did all things when He was upon earth. He rode upon His colt as a king; He reigned upon the rood; He sat at meat with sinners; He wrought tables and chairs at the carpenter's; He fashioned sparrows, as some relate, out of clay, and made them fly; and He said that not a sparrow falls without His love and intention; and He did all and said all in the same spirit and mind, and at the end He smiled and put on His crown again, and sat down for ever *ad dexteram Dei,* that He might let us do the same, and help us by His grace, especially in the sacraments, to be merry and confident.* . . .

This then, too, I thought at that time.

It is marvellous how our Lord sets His seal upon all

* This is a very puzzling philosophy. It is surely either very profound or very shallow. But it certainly is not cynical. Sir John is incapable of such a feeble emotion as that.

that we do, if we will but attend to His working, and not think too highly upon what we do ourselves. He had caused Master Richard to wear His five wounds until he loved them, and to set his meat, too, in their order, and then He had bidden His servant tell him that he did not need the piece of linen, for that he should bear the wounds upon his body. And this He fulfilled; for, as Master Blytchett told me, there were neither more nor less than five wounds upon the young man's body, which he had received from the crowd that set on him, besides the bruises and the stripes. He had caused Master Richard, too, to be haled from judge to judge, as Himself was haled; to be deemed Master by some, and named fool by others; to be borne in a boat by one who loved him; to be arrayed in a white robe to be judged without justice; to be dumb *sicut ovis ad occisionem . . . et quasi agnus coram tondente se** with many other points and marks, besides that which fell afterwards, when a rich man, like him of Arimathy, cared for his burying, and strewed herbs and bay leaves and myrtle upon his body.

There was the matter, too, of the bees that I had seen.† . . .

* "As a sheep to the slaughter . . . as a lamb before his shearer" (Is. liii. 7).

† Sir John lays great stress upon the bees; I cannot understand why. He says that they betokened great wealth and happiness!

And again there was the matter of the seven days that Master Richard fulfilled from the time of his setting out from his house, to the time that he entered into his heavenly mansion. Seven days are the time of perfection; it was in seven days that God Almighty made the world and all that is in it; there were seven years of famine in Egypt in which Joseph gathered store, and seven years of plenty.* . . . And it was in seven days that Master Richard Raynal completed his course, from the sowing of the wheat and wine on Corpus Xti, to his joyful harvest in heaven. . . .]

I thought, too, at this time of many other things, such as you may suppose—of Master Richard's little cell in the country which would never see him again (for I did not know at this time what the King intended of his grace), and of the beasts that awaited him so lamentably, and then of this great room hung all over with royalty whither it had pleased God that his darling should come to die. I looked, too, very often upon Master Richard as he lay before me, upon his clean pallour, paler than I had ever seen it, and his slender fingers roughened by the spade, and his strong arm, and his smiling lips, and his closed eyes that looked within upon what I

* I cannot bring myself to follow Sir John through the whole of the Old and New Testaments.

was not worthy to see, and I wondered often what it was that he was saying to our Lord and the blessed, and what they were saying to him, and I prayed that my name might be mentioned amongst them, lest I should be a castaway after all that I had heard and seen.

When it was dark (for I dared not kindle the candles) the King came in again, and as he came in Master Richard spoke my name, and moved his hand towards me on the coverlet.

XV

How Master Richard went to God

Transivimus per ignem et aquam: et eduxisti nos in refrigerium.

We have passed through fire and water: and Thou hast brought us out into a refreshment.—*Ps. lxv.* 12.

THE King presently kissed Master Richard's hand and asked his pardon and his prayers, saying that he had known nothing of what went forward during those two days, until the crying of Jesus' name by Master Richard before the cardinal, but blaming his own craven heart, as he called it.

And when Master Richard had spoken awhile, he asked the King to go out, for that he had much to say to me in secret.

So the King went out very softly, and set other guards at the doors, and we two sat there a long while.

I was astonished at Master Richard's strength and courage, for he had spoken aloud to the King, but when the King was gone out, he spoke in a lower voice, holding my hand. It was very dark, for he would have no lights, and I could see no more of him but a little of his hair, and the pallour of his face beneath it, until the morn came and the end came.

He told me first of what he had done, and what had been done to him since a week ago, when we had kissed one another at the lychgate—all as I have told it to you. He talked quietly, as I have said, but he laughed a little now and again, and once or twice his voice trembled with tears as he related our Lord's loving-kindness to him. (I have never known any man who loved Jesu Christ more than this man loved Him.)

I asked him a few questions, and he answered them, but the effect of all that he said was what I have written down here, and sometimes I have his very words as he spoke them.

At last he came to the end of what he had to say, and began to tell me of the *Night of the Soul*, and here he talked in a very low voice so that I could scarcely hear what he said, and of what he said I did not understand one half,* for it was full of mysteries such as other con-

* I am thankful that Sir John recognised his own limitations.

templative souls alone would recognize—for all contemplatives, as you know, relate the same things to one
another which they have seen and heard, and the words
that each uses the other understands, but other men do
not; for they speak of things that they have seen indeed,
but for which there are no proper human words, so that
they have to do the best that they can.

He told me that the state that I have described to you
continued until he came before my lord cardinal, so that
although he saw men's faces and heard their words they
were no more to him than shadows and whisperings; for
since (as it appeared to him) he had lost God by his own
fault there was no longer anything by which he might
communicate with man.

Yet all this while there was the conflict of which I
have spoken. There was that in him, which we name the
Will, which continued tense and strong, striving against
despair. Neither his mind nor his heart could help him
in that *Night*; his mind informed him that he had sinned
deadly by presumption, his heart found nowhere God to
love; and all that, though he told himself that God was
loveable, and adorable, and that he could not fall into
hell save by his own purpose and intention.

Yet, in spite of all, and when all had failed him, his

155

will strove against despair (which is the antichrist of humility*), though he did not recognise until afterwards that he was striving, for he thought himself lost, as I have said.

Then a little after noon, at the time when I saw his image at the door of his cell, stretching himself as if after labour or sleep, he had his release.

Now this is the one matter of which he did not tell me fully, nor would he answer when I asked him except by the words, *"Secretum meum mihi."*† But this I know, that he saw our Lord.

And this I know, too, that with that sight his understanding came back to him, and he perceived for himself that Charity was all. He perceived, also, that he had been striving, and amiss. He had striven to bear his own sins, and for those few hours our Lord had permitted him to bear the weight. He who bears heaven and earth upon His shoulders, and who bore the burden of the sins of the world in the garden and upon the rood, had allowed this sweet soul to feel the weight of his own few little sins for those few hours.

When he saw that he made haste to cast them off again upon Him who alone can carry them and live, and to cry

* A curious phrase, and, I think, rather a good one. I suspect it was originally Master Richard's.
† "My secret is mine."

upon His Name; and he understood in that moment, he said, as never before, something of that passion and of the meaning of those five wounds that he had adored so long in ignorance.

But what it was that he saw, and how it was that our Lord shewed Himself, whether on the rood, or as a child with the world in His hands, or as crowned with sharp-thorned roses, or who was with Him, if any were; I do not know. It was then that he said *"Secretum mihi."* And when Master Richard had said that, he added *"Vere languores nostros ipse tulit; et dolores nostros ipse portavit."**

He lay silent a good while after that, and I did not speak to him. When he spoke again, it was to bring to my mind the masses that were to be said, and then he spoke of the Quinte Essence, and said that it was to be mine if I wished for it; and all other things of his were to be mine to do as I pleased with them, for he had no kin in the world.

And after he had spoken of these things the King came in timidly from the parlour, and stood by the door; I could see the pallour of his face against the hangings.

* "Surely He hath borne our infirmities, and carried our sorrows" (Is. liii. 4).

"Come in, my lord King," said Master Richard very faintly. "I have done what was to be done, and there now is nothing but to make an end."

The King knelt down at the further side of the bed.

"Is it the priest you want, Master Hermit?" he asked.

"Sir John will read the prayers presently," said Master Richard.

I heard the King swallow in his throat before he spoke again.

"And you will remember us all," he said, "before God's Majesty, and in particular my poor soul in its passion."

"How could I forget that?" asked Master Richard, and by his voice I knew that he laughed merrily to himself.

I asked him whether he would have lights.

"No, my father," he said, "there will be light enough."

It would be an hour later, I should suppose, after Master Blytchett was come back, when he put out his hand again, and I knew that he wished for the prayers.

Now there was only starlight, for he would have no candles, and the moon was not yet risen. So I went across to the parlour door, and as I went through I could see that the chamber was full of persons all silent, but it was too dark to see who they were. I asked one for a candle, and presently one was brought, and I saw that my lord cardinal was there, and . . . and . . .* and many others. It was such a death-bed as a king might have.

So I read the appointed prayers, kneeling on my knees in the doorway, and I was answered by those behind me.

When I had done that, I stood up to go back, and my lord cardinal caught me by the sleeve.

"For the love of Jesu," he said, "ask if we may come in."

I went back and leaned over Master Richard, taking his hand in my own.

"My lord and the rest desire to come in, my son," I said. "If they may come, press my hand."

He pressed my hand, and I spoke in a low voice, bidding them to come in.

So they came in noiselessly, one after another; I could see their faces moving, but no more—my lord cardinal and the great nobles and the grooms and the rest—till the room was half full of them.

The door was put to behind them, but I could see the line of light that shewed it, where the candle burned in the parlour beyond; and I could hear the sound of their

* The names are omitted as usual. This discreet scribe is very tiresome.

breathing and the rustle once and again of their feet upon the rushes.

Then I knelt down, when the others had knelt, and waited for the agony to begin, when I should begin the last commendation.

My children, I have prayed by many death-beds, but I have never seen one like this.

The curtains were wide, and the windows, behind me, that he might have breath to send out his spirit; and without, as I saw when I turned to kneel, the heavens were bright with stars. This was all the light that was in the room; it was no more than dark twilight, and I could see no more of him than what I saw before, the glimmer of his face upon the pillow and his long hair beside it. His fingers were in mine, but they were very cold by now.

But he had said that there would be light enough, and so there was.

It may have been half an hour afterwards that the room began to lighten softly, as the sky brightened at moonrise, and I could see a little more plainly. His eyes were closed, and he seemed to be breathing very softly through his lips.

Then the moon rose, and the light lay upon the floor at my side. Then a little after it was upon the fringes

160

of the coverlet, and it crept up moment by moment across the leopards and lilies that were broidered in gold and blue.

At last it lay half across the bed, and I could see the King's face very pale and melancholy upon the other side, and Master Blytchett a little behind him.

And presently it reached Master Richard's hand and my own that lay together, but my arm was so numbed that I could feel nothing in it; I could see only that his fingers were in mine.

So the light crept up his arm to the shoulder, and when it reached his face we saw that he was gone to his reward.

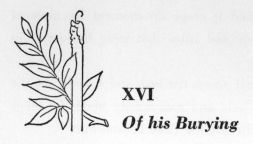

XVI
Of his Burying

Quam dilecta tabernacula tua: Domine virtutum.

How lovely are Thy tabernacles: O Lord of Hosts.—*Ps. lxxxiii.* 1.

IT was upon the next day that we took Master Richard's body down again to the country, and there was such an attendant company as I should not have thought that all London held.

The King had ordered a great plenty of tapers and hangings and a herse such as is used . . .

[*The MS. ends abruptly at the foot of the page.*]